The Fourth State of Matter

Plasma Dynamics and Tomorrow's Technology

BEN BOVA

THE
FOURTH STATE
OF MATTER

Plasma Dynamics and
Tomorrow's Technology

ST. MARTIN'S PRESS   NEW YORK

To Arthur Kantrowitz and the men and women of Avco Everett Research Laboratory.

When you see something that is technically sweet, you go
ahead and do it and you argue about what to do about it only
after you have had your technical success. This is the way it
was with the atomic bomb.

ROBERT OPPENHEIMER

If we only have love
We can melt all the guns
And then give the new world
To our daughters and sons

Then with nothing at all
But the little we are
We'll have conquered all time
All space, the sun, and the stars

JACQUES BREL

Contents

Drawings and Photographs

THE GIFT FROM THE SKY, *lightning, may have started the fires that earliest men first used, and may have given rise to legends such as that of Prometheus. Lightning displays the important features of plasma physics: the interaction of powerful electromagnetic forces with gases. This photograph was made by a Smithsonian Astrophysical Observatory camera that was left with its shutter open for several hours to record any meteors that happened to cross the sky. Instead a thunderstorm came up and left this record of a few hours of lightning discharges. (Smithsonian Astrophysical Observatory)*

ONE

The Gift from the Sky

This is the story of a young science, and of a new technology that will change your life.

The science is plasma physics. And the technology that is coming from plasma physics can help to build a world that's free from hunger and want, free from pollution, a world in which man can generate all the energy he needs to run his civilization and yet still live in harmony with the environment, a world in which man can set out in earnest for the farthest reaches of the solar system and perhaps even challenge the stars themselves.

But this beautiful world of the future won't come about by itself, automatically. If it happens at all, it will be because men and women make it happen. To a large extent, it's up to you. Even if you don't intend to be a scientist or engineer, you will be a voter and your decisions can help to shape the future of all technology. Informed, thoughtful citizens can make certain that the benefits of science and technology are used wisely, for the good of all the people. Those who ignore science and technology, who dismiss it as something beyond their grasp, are doomed to have others make their decisions for them. This book is an introduction to plasma physics and technology, written to give you a glimpse of a possible future—*your* future—so that you can make up your own mind about this exciting new science.

1

Plasma is a fourth state of matter, quite different from the solids, liquids and gases we're familiar with. Most people don't even realize that plasmas exist. When they think of a fluorescent lamp, they don't realize that it's plasma energy that makes it bright. When a rocket bellows off its launching pad, it's plasma streaming from the exhaust nozzles, not gas. When a nuclear bomb spreads its searing fireball, it's plasma that's destroying everything it touches.

Rockets that carry bold men into space, and nuclear fireballs that spread death—these are two excellent symbols for the promise and danger of plasma technology. The same power that offers us such a bright future can also put an end to all the future. Like all technology, the promise of plasma science can be used either way. Much has been written on the dangers of technology. In this book we'll examine some of the brighter promises of plasma science. They can make a future that's worth working toward.

The story of plasmas begins in the very ancient past. Like all of man's endeavors, plasma science didn't spring up suddenly out of nowhere. The physicists and engineers of today who are trying to understand and utilize plasmas, are merely the present-day actors in a long and fascinating drama.

The story begins with lightning. And fire.

Fire was man's first source of energy outside of his own body. And fire was most probably the gift of a plasma-generating lightning stroke.

The discovery of fire is such an important event in man's history that nearly every culture on Earth has built up a mythology about it. To the ancient Greeks it was Prometheus who defied the Olympians and brought fire to man. To the Germanic and Norse peoples it was Loki. To the American Indians, it was one of their animal totems, Coyote or Rabbit or another, depending on the particular tribe reciting the myth.

Regardless of the name or form of the godlike creature who brought fire to man, the legends are much the same. Before the gift of fire, man was a weak, cold, hungry, miserable specimen, little better than the animals of the fields. Then, at great cost to himself, Prometheus/Loki/Coyote stole fire from the heavens and gave it to man. Thus began man's civilization and his eventual domination of the world.

Like most myths, the legend of the fire-bringer is fantastic in detail and absolutely correct in spirit. Anthropologists who have sifted through the fossil remains of early man have drawn a picture that's considerably less romantic, yet still startlingly close to the essence of the myth.

The first evidence of man's use of fire dates back roughly half a million years. The hero of the story is hardly godlike in appearance. He is *Homo erectus*, an ancestor of ours who lived in Africa, Asia and possibly Europe during the warm millenia between the second and third glaciations of the Ice Age. *Homo erectus* was scarcely five feet tall. His skull was rather halfway between the shape of an ape's and our own. His brain case was only two-thirds of our size. But his body was fully human: he walked erect and had human, grasping hands.

And he must have had other attributes we'd recognize as human: curiosity and courage.

Fire was a gift from the sky, the myths must be correct about that. Most likely a bolt of lightning set a tree or bush afire, and an especially curious and courageous member of the *Homo erectus* species overcame his very natural fear to reach out for the bright warm energy of the flames. No telling how many times our ancestors got their fingers burned for their troubles. But eventually they learned to handle fire safely, and to use it.

With fire, man's technology was born.

Each new phase of that technology's growth has been marked by finding newer, more potent sources of energy. Simple wood fires gave way to coal and coke, and allowed men to begin smelting metals. Steam replaced animal and human muscles (eliminating slavery), only to be replaced itself, in time, by electricity and internal-combustion engines. Turbines and rockets are now powering our most advanced means of transportation. Nuclear energy is being harnessed to provide electricity.

Technology has allowed man to spread his civilization across the world. It's made him master of this planet and turned his eyes to other worlds. But it's also brought man to the point where he threatens to destroy his home world—destroy it with bombs, with overpopulation, or with pollution.

Plasmas are the next step in this spiral of new, richer sources of power. But for the first time in ages, man has found a power source that needn't gut this planet further. Plasma technology can—if used wisely—solve man's constant need for more power *and at the same time* end the pollution that threatens to choke us in our own wastes.

That's what this book is all about.

In the pages that follow, we'll look at a few of the many aspects of plasma physics. For the most part, we'll be dealing with plasma *dynamics,* the actions of plasmas in motion. The next chapter will be mainly historical, to show some of the basics of plasma science and introduce a few of the interesting men who've contributed their work to this field.

Next, we'll see how the behavior of plasmas helped to shape the creation of the solar system, and how plasma reactions govern the ultimate death of a star. Then we'll take a closer look at the plasma in interplanetary space today, just a few hundred kilometers over our heads, and see how it affects our planet and our lives.

In the following chapters we'll concentrate on what plasma technology can do for us, mainly in two vital areas: generating electrical power without pollution, and enhancing our ability to explore the solar system and the universe beyond. In the final chapter we'll take a look at the brightest promise of all: controlled thermonuclear reactors, the dream of harnessing the power of the stars to satisfy forever man's search for new sources of energy.

Now a few words on what this book is not.

It's not a textbook, and there will be very little mathematics in the pages that follow. It's not an exhaustive review of every aspect of plasma physics; that would take a library full of books to do properly. This book is merely an introduction to a few chosen aspects of plasma physics. It's a quick glimpse at a world that you may find fascinating.

At the back of this book there are some suggestions for further reading. There are also appendices to explain the numbering systems and terminology used in the chapters that follow.

If, at the end of this book, you want to learn more about this exciting world of plasma physics, fine. There's much to learn, much to accomplish. On the other hand, if you put this book down with nothing more than the realization that technology—in the hands of thoughtful people—can help to solve many of the problems created by the thoughtless technological decisions of yesterday, then this book will have accomplished its purpose.

TWO

The Fourth State of Matter

The ancients believed that the universe was made of four substances—earth, air, fire and water.

Modern scientists say that matter can exist in four conditions, or states—solid, liquid, gas or plasma.

You've known about the first three states of matter all your life. But outside of the ranks of professional scientists and their students, very few people even today realize that a fourth state of matter exists. The word *plasma* has a rather indistinct but intriguing meaning. It comes from an old Greek root, *plassein,* which means "to shape or mold." As used today, *plasma* means something unformed, something waiting to be shaped or molded by outside forces. The clear, formless liquid part of blood is called plasma. The shapeless blobs of living matter that make up the cells in all living creatures, are called protoplasm. And in 1928, the American physical chemist Irving Langmuir (1881–1957) coined this ancient word anew to describe the fourth state of matter.

What's so different about a plasma that it deserves to be considered separately from solids, liquids and gases? A plasma looks like a gas and in many ways behaves like a gas. But there's a major difference: a plasma is a gas that conducts electricity.

That doesn't look like much of a difference, at first glance. But don't be fooled. On such seemingly slight differences are built the universe—and tomorrow's technology.

Down to the Molecules

To understand what's so significant about plasmas, we'll have to know something about the other three states of matter.

You know that all matter is made of *atoms*. And atoms can combine into groups called *molecules*. A molecule may be as simple as the two-atom combination of oxygen (O_2) or nitrogen (N_2). Or it may be as complex as the double helix of deoxyribonucleic acid (DNA), the basic molecular structure of all life on Earth, a molecule that contains millions of atoms.

In a solid, the molecules are set rigidly into a crystal structure, often called a *lattice*. The situation is very much like an auditorium full of people, when everyone is sitting in chairs and nobody's walking around the aisles. Each person can fidget, shuffle his feet, scratch his nose; but nobody gets out of his chair. In a solid, the molecules vibrate, but they stay in place in their crystal lattice. They do not meander.

Suppose the solid we're talking about is ice. Now add some heat. It begins to melt. Looking back at our auditorium full of people, we can say that some of the people are now getting out of their seats and walking around. When the ice melts completely into liquid water, the situation in the auditorium is that all the people are up and moving around, and their chairs have disappeared. The crystal lattice structure no longer exists in the liquid state. All the molecules can roam around.

Add more heat and the water begins to boil, to turn into a gas called steam. In our analogy of the auditorium, we can see that now many of the people are leaving the auditorium, bolting through the doors and heading off in all directions. In a gas, the molecules can move independently of one another. Except for outright collisions, the molecules exert no influence on each other. It's every molecule for himself in a gas.

Notice what had to be done to change the solid into a liquid and the liquid into a gas. We added energy. In this case, the energy was in the form of heat. As we'll see further on in this book, heat energy is one of the easiest forms to produce and use.

When Aristotle tried to describe the universe with a neat and comprehensible system, he arranged the four substances in an orderly fashion. He placed earth at the bottom of the universe, because it was the heaviest and least mobile of the four substances. Water came next, since it was more mobile, and above water came air. Obviously. Anyone can see the common sense in that. Above the air was the realm of fire, which we poor mortals can only see in glimpses, such as the blazing brilliance of the sun, or the flash of lightning, or the tiny sparks of the stars.

A neat and comprehensible system. We may smile at its naive assumptions, but Aristotle's system satisfied man's craving for order for more than a thousand years.

And although he may not have had the benefits of modern science, Aristotle was certainly on the right track. He had correctly arranged the solids, liquids and gases in the order of their energy content. And he even put plasmas (fire) in the right place, nearly two thousand years before anyone dreamed that there was a fourth state of matter.

It wasn't until late in the nineteenth century that scientists began to guess that a fourth state of matter might exist. Two fields of knowledge were needed before physicists could begin to understand plasmas. First, they had to know the physics of ordinary gases. Second, they had to understand the physics of electromagnetic forces. For like the lightning bolt, plasma physics combines gas physics and electromagnetics.

Toward Plasmas: Gas Physics

Gas physics began, like so much of all physics, with Galileo and his students in the seventeenth century. Evangelista Torricelli (1608–1647), for example, proved that air has weight, just as solids and liquids do. This is not an obvious truth, and came as a considerable surprise to many Renaissance thinkers. As a by-product of his research, Torricelli invented the barometer, which is still a basic tool of weather forecasters.

For the next two centuries, physicists and chemists slowly built up an understanding of the behavior of gases. The line between physics and chemistry was never a clear-cut partition, but for the

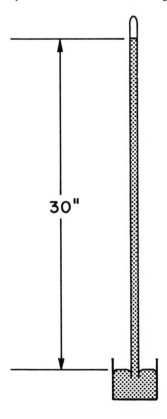

30"

TORRICELLI'S EXPERIMENT *proved that air has weight, a new idea in the seventeenth century. The long glass tube is filled with mercury and then stood on its open end in the dish. The mercury spills out into the dish until only a column of mercury 30 inches high is left in the tube. The weight of the air on the surface of the open pool in the dish balances the weight of the mercury still in the tube. This phenomenon is the basis for the modern barometer, which foretells weather conditions by showing slight changes in air pressure.*

most part the men we would call physicists were interested in the over-all behavior of gases, while the chemists worried mainly about the microscopic structure of gases.

While the nations of Europe were spreading empires through the Americas, Africa and Asia, while Britain and France fought the long series of wars that culminated at Waterloo, while the United States won its independence and struggled to establish a new form of government—a chain of scientists, British and French for the most part, were patiently and laboriously unravelling the secrets of gas physics.

The major links in this chain of men were Robert Boyle (1627–1691), Jacques Alexandre César Charles (1746–1823), the American-born Benjamin Thompson (1753–1814) who became Count Rumford of England, John Dalton (1766–1844), Amedeo Avogadro of Italy (1776–1856), Joseph Gay-Lussac (1778–1850), James Prescott Joule (1818–1889), and James Clerk Maxwell (1831–1879). Underlying all their researches was the enormous contribution of Sir Isaac Newton (1642–1727), whose formulation of the laws of motion and gravity gave a firm foundation to all of physics.

The understanding that these men evolved came to be known as the *kinetic theory of gases*. The fact that it's called a theory doesn't mean it's unproved. The kinetic theory is the basic underpinning of man's knowledge of gases. It can be summed up in four statements:

1. *Gases are composed of very large numbers of particles.* Before Boyle's time, most people believed that gases were smooth, continuous clouds of ephemeral matter with no internal structure whatsoever. Certainly, gases don't appear to be made of particles, they don't feel grainy. But, starting with Boyle's experiments, scientists were gradually able to show that gases are indeed made of particles, huge numbers of very tiny particles. In a cubic centimeter of air at 0° Centigrade (the freezing point of water) and a pressure of one atmosphere (sea level pressure) there are 2.45×10^{19} molecules. That's more than 24 billion *billion* molecules in a space the size of a sugar cube.

Most common gases are composed of molecules. Some elements such as helium, neon and argon are composed of atoms. These so-called *inert gases* do not form molecules except under very special circumstances. The inert gases are also sometimes called the *noble gases,* since they stand aloof from all molecule combinations. They are also called atomic gases, as opposed to molecular gases.

Air is a mixture of many elements and compounds. It contains about 80% molecular nitrogen (N_2), nearly 20% molecular oxygen (O_2), a variable amount of water vapor (H_2O), and traces of carbon dioxide (CO_2) and inert gases such as argon (A), neon (Ne) and krypton (Kr).

2. *The molecules in a gas are in constant random motion, and their motions can be described by Newton's laws.* The most dramatic proof of this assumption came from, of all people, a botanist. Robert Brown of Scotland (1773–1858) was studying tiny spores of pollen in a microscope in 1827. He saw that the spores were in a constant state of agitation, always moving, jumping about. At first he thought that the spores were animated by some life force inherent in the them. Then he found that dust particles and even soot grains acted the same way.

The spores were being jostled by swarms of invisible particles, molecules of gas too small to be seen even in Brown's microscope. The effect came to be called *Brownian Motion.* Incidentally, although his accidental discovery gave him a certain measure of immortality, Brown's most important discovery came four years later. In 1831 he deduced that all living cells have a nucleus. This was the beginning of modern biochemistry.

The molecules in a gas are in constant, hectic motion. In air at 0°C, the molecules are roaring along at speeds of 1600 kilometers per hour, or better than 43,000 centimeters per second. However, they hardly get to travel any distance at all before colliding with a neighboring molecule. With 2.45×10^{19} molecules per cubic centimeter, even the very tiny particles will constantly collide with each other.

On the average, under standard conditions (0°C temperature and 1 atmosphere pressure) the molecules are only about 3.34×10^{-7} centimeter apart from each other. In one second a molecule will make five billion collisions with its neighbors, travelling an average of only 10^{-5} centimeter before suffering a collision. This distance that the average molecule travels between collisions is called the *mean free path* of the molecule.

Although the average molecule may not get far in its hectic, collision-filled travels, the total travel mileage logged by the molecules is stupendous. In one second, the molecules in a cubic centimeter of air will travel a total of nearly 1.3×10^{19} kilometers—roughly 300,000 times farther than the distance between the sun and the next star, Alpha Centauri!

3. *The size of each molecule is extremely small, and therefore the volume actually occupied by all the molecules is a small fraction of the space ordinarily considered to be occupied by the gas.* You can jam several people into a telephone booth; say, five or six. But they can't move around very much. Take the same half-dozen people and make a basketball team out of them, and you need a gymnasium to hold them. The same is true for molecules.

Take oxygen as an example. Under ordinary conditions here on Earth, oxygen is a gas. But if you chill it down to $-183°C$ ($90.1°K$ or $-297.4°F$) oxygen will turn into a liquid. Its liquid volume is nearly 800 times less than its volume as a gas, even though the same number of molecules are present.

The oxygen molecule is 2.4×10^{-8} centimeter in diameter. If you could take a flash photograph with a super-camera that could stop the motion of the molecules in a gas, you would see billions upon billions of molecules hanging in space with nothing, absolute emptiness, between them. There is much more emptiness in a gas than there are molecules. But because the molecules are in such violent motion, the gas takes up much more space than the molecules would need if they were stilled.

4. *The molecules in a gas behave as hard elastic spheres. There are no forces of attraction or repulsion except when molecules collide. No energy of motion is lost through collisions between molecules, although energy may be transferred from one molecule to another in a collision.* That sounds like a lot to digest, but it can be easily pictured if you think of the molecules as being similar to billiard balls. But you must imagine billions of billiard balls rushing pell-mell through three-dimensional space, smashing into one another with untiring blind fury.

When two molecules collide, the total amount of energy they had between them before the collision remains the same after the collision. But the distribution of energy between the two molecules might change. A fast-moving molecule may come out of a collision travelling more slowly. But if it does, then its collision-partner is going faster than it was before the crash. The distribution of energy might change, but the total amount of energy always stays the same.

When a molecule strikes the wall of a solid that is holding the gas, there is no loss of energy at all. The molecule bounces off the wall with exactly the same amount of energy that it had before the collision. Such collisions are said to be *perfectly elastic*.

Summary: The world of gases looks like chaos. The molecules are hurtling in all directions in a gas, smashing into their neighbors in an unending rush hour of frenzied violence. Except for these collisions, there is no interaction between molecules. One molecule does not attract another, does not bend it out of its normal straight-line path, does not influence it by gravity or electromagnetic force or anything else. Collisions are the only interaction among the molecules of a gas. It's like a madhouse version of highway traffic on a holiday weekend, with the exception that the collisions don't damage the molecules at all.

The kinetic theory of gases actually describes an *ideal gas* that exists only in theory. Real gases in the real world vary to some extent from this ideal. But the kinetic theory works well enough to allow engineers to design airplanes and vacuum cleaners, air conditioners and suspension bridges—all based on the madhouse of the molecules.

Toward Plasmas: Electricity in Gases

Lord Ernest Rutherford (1871–1937), the man who discovered the structure of the atom, was taught the billiard-ball picture of gases when he was a student. "I was brought up to look at the atom as a nice hard fellow, red or grey in color, according to taste," he once said. Rutherford showed that this view of the atom was far from accurate. But the billiard-ball picture does serve an important purpose: it adequately describes the behavior of particles in a gas.

Up to a point.

By the second half of the nineteenth century, that point had been reached. Physicists were ready and anxious to probe deeper into the structure of gases, liquids and solids, to determine what molecules and atoms really looked like.

In probing into the structure of molecules and atoms, one promising line of attack seemed to be the study of electrical effects in gases. No one deliberately set out to discover a fourth state of matter; it was the inner structure of those "billiard balls" that the physicists were after.

From the beginning of man's study of electricity, there's been something wild and exciting about the subject. The classic scene, of course, is Benjamin Franklin (1706–1790) standing in the thunderstorm, a key attached to his kite string, proving that lightning and electricity are one and the same. Up to that point, most people thought lightning was quite different from "animal electricity," as it was often called in those days. After all, the only sources of manmade electricity in the eighteenth century look like parlor tricks to us today. You could rub a glass rod with silk or fur and create a spark of static electricity if you brought the rod close to a metal object. Static electricity could also be induced and stored in insulated vessels such as Leyden jars.

A few experimenters were developing the primitive ancestors of today's batteries. Among these workers were the Italians Luigi Galvani (1737–1798) and Allesandro Volta (1745–1827). They were good friends, despite the fact that they argued on opposite sides of the issue of "animal electricity."

Galvani discovered that the legs of dead frogs could be made to twitch when they came in contact with a source of electricity, such as a Leyden jar or one of his primitive electrical cells (batteries). Please realize that there was no knowledge of how electrical currents work. No one could say for sure if the electricity was going from the jar or cell into the frog's leg, or if there was electricity already in the leg that somehow became activated by coming in contact with the jar or cell.

Galvani experimented extensively with "animal electricity" and became convinced that electricity was inherent in the animal tissue itself.

Not so, said his good friend, Count Volta. He duplicated Galvani's experiments and concluded—correctly—that electricity was flowing from the outside source into the animal tissue. Good friends though they were, they argued the point with Latin passion for many years. Gradually Volta's view prevailed throughout the scientific world, although the debate wasn't really settled until after both men died. Volta, of course, was honored by having the *volt* named after him.

Meanwhile, in England, Michael Faraday (1791–1867) was quietly changing history. He invented the first electrical power generator, which was dramatically called the "dynamo." Thanks to his work, man eventually became able to generate the huge amounts of electrical power that run our technological society of today.

But in Faraday's own time, the dynamo was little more than a laboratory curiosity. It hardly seemed like a machine that would change the world. Legend has it that Faraday once gave a lecture to a group of London citizens on the scientific work he was doing. Naturally, he described his work on the dynamo. After his speech, a woman asked him, "What you said was all very interesting, but of what use is it?" Faraday replied with a line that's become a byword for all research scientists: "Madam, of what use is a newborn baby?"

The main figure tying together gas physics with electromagnetics was James Clerk Maxwell. In fact, the very term *electromagnetism* stems from his work. We've already seen that Maxwell was a major contributor to the kinetic theory of gases. He also laid down the theoretical foundation for an understanding of electromagnetic forces. He showed that electricity and magnetism were two facets of the same force, and that light and heat radiation are both forms of electromagnetic energy. Nine years after his untimely death at 48, when radio waves were discovered, Maxwell's solid framework of electromagnetic theory formed the backbone upon which modern electronic communications has been built.

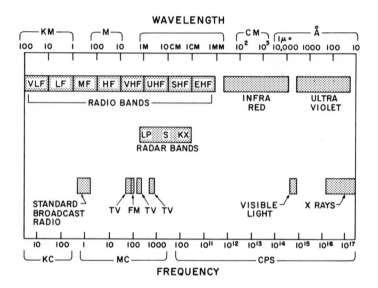

THE ELECTROMAGNETIC SPECTRUM *includes radio waves, infrared radiation, visible light, ultraviolet radiation, x-rays and the even-shorter gamma rays (not shown here). Note that the waves can be described either by wavelength or frequency. Long wavelengths are equivalent to low frequencies. Thus a radio wave with a wavelength of one kilometer has a frequency of one million cycles per second: a million such waves would pass a fixed point each second. This frequency is called 1 megacycle (MC) or 1 megahertz.*

Working with little more than a pencil and paper, Maxwell uncovered the basic nature of electrical and magnetic *fields.*

You know that the influence of a magnet goes beyond the solid body of the magnet itself. If you place a magnet close enough to a piece of iron or steel (say a paper clip) the clip will be drawn to the magnet even though nothing visible touches it or moves it. Spread a sheet of paper over a magnet and sprinkle some iron filings on the paper and you see the *magnetic field* that extends from the magnet's poles. Take two magnets and hold them so that their north (or south) poles are facing each other and then try to force them to touch together. You will feel a rubbery, invisible, but quite strong force holding the two magnets apart.

There are electrical fields, too, and they share most of the characteristics of magnetic fields. When you rub a rubber comb until it's well charged with static electricity and then pick up scraps of paper with it, you will find that the paper begins moving toward the comb just as the steel clip moves toward the magnet. An *electric field* affects the paper even though the comb doesn't touch the paper. When you brush your hair hard on a very dry day, so that some individual hairs stand out on end, they're being held against the gravitational pull of the whole Earth by an electric field induced in your hair.

Maxwell showed that electric and magnetic fields are interlinked. Every moving electrical charge generates both an electric field and a magnetic field. Usually the two are considered as a single electromagnetic field. Maxwell showed that electromagnetic waves exist—waves of pure energy with no physical matter connected to them. The phenomenon we call light is one type of electromagnetic wave, one slice out of a huge spectrum of energy waves that encompass radio frequencies, infrared radiation, visible light, ultraviolet, x-rays and gamma rays.

Electromagnetic waves can travel through empty space. Visible light, radio emissions and other forms of electromagnetic energy travel from the stars across vast distances of near-perfect vacuum. And all electromagnetic waves travel at the same speed in a vacuum: 300,000 kilometers per second. We call it the speed of light. It's also the speed of radio waves and all electromagnetic energy.

All electromagnetic forces obey the *inverse square rule*. That is, their strength decreases in proportion to the square of the distance from the source. Thus, if you see two street lamps, and the second is twice as far away as the first, its brightness will be one-quarter of the first lamp's brightness. A third lamp, three times farther off than the first one, will be one-ninth as bright.

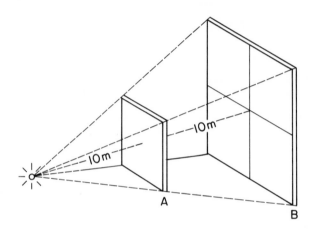

THE INVERSE SQUARE RULE *states that the intensity of radiation decreases with the square of the distance. The light shown would appear one-fourth as bright when the distance is doubled. All electromagnetic radiation, and gravity, follows the inverse square rule.*

Armed with the knowledge of Maxwell and Faraday and many other researchers, physicists in the latter half of the nineteenth century began to probe into the atomic structure of matter by studying electrical effects in gases.

Ordinarily, gases will not conduct an electrical current. In fact, gases usually make very good electrical insulators. If room-temperature air conducted electricity easily, for example, this would be an extremely dangerous world! But only under very unusual conditions can gases be made to conduct electricity.

Sir William Crookes (1832–1919) was among the first to investigate electrical effects in gases. He used a piece of apparatus called the *glow-discharge tube,* and perfected its use to the point where it was often called the Crookes tube. The glow-discharge tube is very similar to the fluorescent lamps we're familiar with today. The gas inside the tube is drawn out by a vacuum pump until the remaining gas is at a very low pressure. Under these conditions, an electrical current can be forced through the gas. The rarified gas in the tube glows when excited by the electrical energy, and the color of the glow depends mainly on the particular type of gas being used. Each gas gives off its own characteristic colors. This eventually led to today's garish advertising signs.

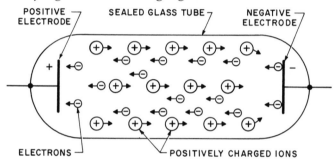

THE GLOW DISCHARGE TUBE *was a basic tool of physicists in early studies of plasmas. In the tube an electrical current flows between the two electrodes and the gas "breaks down" into positively-charged ions and free electrons, which are negatively charged. Modern fluorescent lamps use the same principle.*

The beautiful glow in Crookes' tubes came from individual atoms within the rarified gas, and thus the glow-discharge tube was a convenient way to study some aspects of the behavior of individual atoms. Apparently Crookes realized that the electrified gas in the tube was no longer truly a gas. In 1879 he concluded that it was actually a fourth state of matter.

Many physicists followed in Crookes' path, but they weren't particularly interested in a fourth state of matter. They were seeking out the structure of the atom. A giant in this field of research was Sir Joseph John Thomson (1856–1940). In 1897 he discovered the existence of the electron and correctly identified it as a particle that ordinarily exists within the atom. Under the conditions in the glow tube, however, electrons are freed from their parent atoms and flow independently of them. Thomson measured the mass and electrical charge of the electron, and in 1906 received the Nobel Prize in physics.

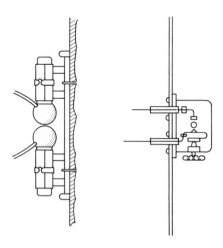

HERTZ'S EQUIPMENT *proved that electromagnetic waves other than light can be created at will and transmitted over a distance without wires. His transmitter (left) created a rapidly oscillating spark between the two metal spheres. Across the room, a similar spark sprang up in the gap between the sphere and cone of his receiver.*

More important than any prize, though, was the fact that man had at last opened up the atom. For the first time, physicists showed that the atom is not an indivisible "billiard ball." It consists of still-smaller particles.

The electron bore a negative electrical charge. The atoms that lost electrons carried positive electrical charges. When an electron was part of the atom, of course, the atom was electrically neutral. Thomson believed that the atom's structure was simply spherical, with the electrons stuck into the atom "like raisins in a cake." Rutherford proved otherwise. Using completely different techniques, Rutherford showed in 1911 that the atom consists of a very tiny core, or *nucleus*, with the electrons orbiting around it. In 1908

Rutherford was awarded the Nobel Prize in chemistry for his work in radioactivity. Being a physicist, he was both amused and embarrassed by the Nobel Committee's classification of his work.

Rutherford's work marked a dividing point in physics. He didn't use the glow-tube technique. Most of the physicists interested in dissecting the inner structure of the atomic nucleus followed Rutherford's path, and left gas physics behind them. They blazed a new trail, one that led to nuclear fission, atomic bombs, and presently to nuclear electric power generators. But, as we'll see later, the path of the nuclear physicists reconnected with the path of gas and plasma physics after a separation of nearly 30 years.

And while the excitement of probing the atom moved away from gas physics, other things were happening that made the study of electrical effects in gases equally exciting. We'll have to backtrack a little, and return to Maxwell's work for a moment.

Maxwell showed theoretically that electromagnetic waves exist and travel through space. They can also travel through liquids, solids and gases, depending on the wavelength of the energy and the matter in question. Visible light, for example, can travel through air and water, and even through some solids such as glass and clear plastics. Maxwell's work predicted that there were all sorts of electromagnetic waves, invisible to us. But until 1888, no one had ever detected such waves.

The German physicist Heinrich Hertz (1857–1894) changed all that. The youthful Hertz set up a simple yet elegant experiment. His equipment produced an electric spark between two metal balls that were separated by a slight air gap. The spark crackled back and forth through the gap. Maxwell's equations predicted that the spark should produce invisible electromagnetic waves. Across the room from the first piece of equipment (which we now call a *transmitter*) Hertz placed a simple loop of wire, with an equally small gap in it. When the spark generated electromagnetic waves in the transmitter, the waves should travel across the room and induce an electric current in the wire loop (called the *receiver*), causing a similar spark to flicker in its air gap.

A simple experiment. And it worked. Hertz proved conclusively that electromagnetic waves other than light can be created at will and transmitted over a distance without wires or any other physical connection. Hertz had built the first radio.

In today's world of color television and communications satellites, it's difficult to realize how earth-shaking Hertz's experiment was. The excitement over "Hertzian waves" was tremedous throughout the technical world. Man could transmit energy through space!

The so-called "Hertzian waves" are what we know today as *radio waves*. Hertz calculated that the waves produced by his first transmitter were a meter or so long, some ten million times longer than light waves, which are from 3.5 to 8×10^{-7} meter in length.

Seven years later, in 1895, Wilhelm Roentgen (1845–1923) discovered a very different type of electromagnetic radiation. These waves, at first called *Roentgen rays*, were shorter than light waves; they were typically around 10^{-10} meter in wavelength. And the radiation penetrated solid matter! Very much baffled by this strange discovery, Roentgen himself dubbed the radiation *x-rays*. The most convenient way to generate x-rays, even today, is by driving an electric current through a vacuum tube, not too different from the glow-discharge tubes of Crookes and Thomson.

Things were happening quickly now. While Roentgen was puzzling over the nature of x-rays, an Italian physicist named Guglielmo Marconi (1874–1937) was developing improved transmitters and receivers of Hertzian waves. In 1901 he successfully transmitted a radio signal across the Atlantic Ocean. The era of wireless electronic communications was born.

But wait. Most physicists were startled by Marconi's success, because Maxwell's worked showed that radio waves would not bend over the horizon, any more than light waves turn around corners. Marconi's radio transmission should have sailed off into space. How did the radio waves bend around the Earth's curvature and get across the ocean?

In 1902, an American electrical engineer and an English physicist both proposed an answer to this problem. The American was Arthur Kennely (1861–1939); the Englishman, Oliver Heaviside

(1850–1925). As happens often in science, neither man knew of the other's work when he proposed his solution to the problem.

Kennely and Heaviside both suggested that there was a layer of

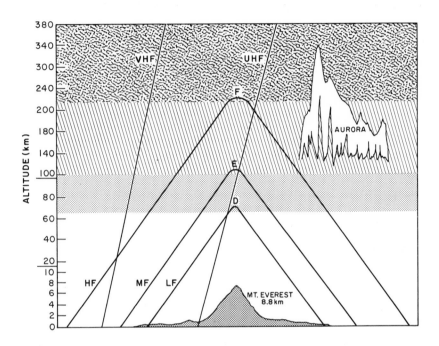

THE IONOSPHERE *consists of various layers of ionized gases—plasmas —that reflect certain radio frequencies. The altitudes of the different layers vary considerably from day to day, depending largely on the activity of the sun. Low, medium and high frequency radio waves are reflected at different altitudes, and thus allow long-range radio broadcasts to span oceans and continents. But very high frequency and ultra high frequency—which are used for television broadcasts —are not reflected by the ionosphere. Thus TV signals can only be sent as far as the horizon, unless they are relayed. The aurorae are thought to be caused by ions and electrons of the ionosphere that are excited to the point where they glow. (Note that the altitude scale in this chart is logarithmic, which exaggerates the height of Mt. Everest greatly.)*

electrified gases high up in the Earth's atmosphere that reflected radio waves. This was quickly found to be true, and that region of the atmosphere was soon named the *Kennely–Heaviside layer.* Nowadays it's often shortened to the Heaviside layer, somewhat unfairly to Kennely. More often it's called by the impartial term, *the ionosphere,* for reasons we'll go into in a moment.

With the advent of practical electronic communications, half a century's worth of patient research began to pay off handsomely. The study of electrical effects in gases and the years of investigation into glow-discharge phenomena, became the cornerstone of electronics engineering.

The research contributed to radio communications on two fronts. First, there was constant work toward making better vacuum tubes. Offspring of the glow-discharge tubes, the vacuum tubes quickly became the heart of radio equipment, supplanted only half a century later by transistors. Even today, though, the cathode ray tubes that form the heart of your TV set are direct descendants of J. J. Thomson's work and that of his followers.

The other contribution made by research was a growing understanding of the ionosphere: its structure, and how radio waves of different frequencies are either reflected, absorbed, or pass right through its various layers. It was soon realized that the ionosphere consisted of gas that was *ionized,* somewhat like the gas in a glow discharge. That is, there were free electrons and positive ions instead of electrically neutral atoms. Hence the name *ionosphere.* Researchers also found that the conditions in the ionosphere were largely controlled by the sun, and events on the sun such as sunspots and solar flares can cause violent fluctuations in the ionosphere. These fluctuations, in turn, can raise havoc with radio reception around the world. We'll see more about the sun's effect on Earth in Chapter 4.

By the 1920's, radio communication was big business. Large industrial research laboratories such as the General Electric Laboratories in Schenectady, N.Y., were deeply engaged in investigating the basic physical phenomena of radio communications, and seeking ways to make better electronic equipment.

It was at the GE labs that Irving Langmuir (1881–1957) carried out basic studies of electrified gases in vacuum tubes. Like Crookes half a century earlier, Langmuir realized that the matter inside the glow discharge was different from ordinary gases. In 1928, Langmuir coined the term *plasma*. The fourth state of matter finally had a name of its own.

Langmuir, incidentally, was an unusually versatile scientist. He's widely known in physics for his work with plasmas. In 1932 he won a Nobel Prize in chemistry for studies of molecular chemical effects that have had important applications in medical research. Toward the end of his life he pioneered experiments on weather modification, and was the guiding force behind the first successful cloud seeding in which man-made snow was produced.

The World of Plasmas

We saw earlier that one prime difference between gases and plasmas is that plasmas can conduct electricity. Now it's time to look deeper into that seemingly simple difference.

You recall that the differences between solids, liquids and gases were basically a matter of the energy stored in the molecules. Of the three "ordinary" states of matter, gases are much more energetic than liquids or solids. Plasmas have even more energy invested in them than gases do. And while the kinetic theory of gases can explain the large-scale behavior of gases perfectly well, we're going to need a more detailed look into the atom before we can understand the behavior of plasmas.

Rutherford showed that the atom consists of a small nucleus surrounded by orbiting electrons. For each chemical element there is a different atom.

Atomic nuclei contain two types of particles: *protons,* which carry a positive electrical charge; and *neutrons,* which are electrically neutral. Electrons are charged negatively. For each proton in an atom's nucleus, there is an electron in orbit around the nucleus. Hydrogen, the lightest element, consists of nothing more than one proton for a nucleus and one electron in orbit around it. Helium has a nucleus of two protons and two neutrons, with two orbital electrons. The heavy element uranium has 92 protons in its nucleus, together with 146 neutrons, and 92 electrons orbiting that nucleus. Thus, for every atom, there are as many electrons as there are protons, and the atom's electrical charges are balanced out. The atom is neutral.

But not in a plasma.

If enough energy is put into an atom, one or more of its electrons will tear free, like an orbiting spacecraft that fires its thrusters and heads off for deep space. If one electron leaves the atom, there will be a proton in the nucleus whose positive charge is no longer balanced by a negative electron. The atom will have a net positive charge. It's no longer electrically neutral. It's then called an *ion*.

Although there are conditions where a negative ion can be created by adding an extra electron to an atom, we'll be considering only positive ions in this book. So whenever we mention an ion, it will be a positively-charged body, the remainder of an atom after one or more of its electrons have been removed from it.

The process of removing electrons from atoms is called *ionization*. Long before Langmuir coined the term plasma, physicists were talking about ionized gases. One dictionary-type definition for a plasma is simply, a gas that is ionized.

If an atom has more than one electron, it can be ionized to varying degrees. The oxygen atom, for instance, has eight electrons. If it loses one electron, it's said to be singly ionized. If it loses two, it's doubly ionized, and so forth until all eight electrons are gone and the oxygen atom is completely ionized. There's nothing left then but the bare nucleus; all eight electrons have gone.

Gone where?

In a plasma, the electrons merely take up independent lives of their own. They can be considered as separate particles, almost like the billiard balls we talked about in our discussion of the kinetic theory of gases. Most plasmas consist of free electrons, positive ions, and some still-neutral atoms. A plasma may be lightly ionized, and the neutral atoms outnumber the electrons and ions. Or a plasma may be fully ionized, and there are no neutral atoms in it at all.

Because there's a free negative electron for every positive charge in the ions, a plasma *as a whole* is electrically neutral. But those free electrons can carry electrical currents. And both the ions and electrons can be shaped, molded, moved and energized by electromagnetic forces. In fact, the truly major difference between a gas and a plasma is that the particles in a plasma *can exert electromagnetic forces on each other.*

We saw that the particles in a gas don't influence each other at all, except in collisions. But in a plasma, the electrons and ions can exert electromagnetic forces on each other. Such forces of attraction or repulsion are called *Coulomb forces,* after the French physicist Charles Augustin de Coulomb (1736–1806) who studied the forces of electrical attraction and repulsion.

This is why plasmas are different from gases. They have many of the properties of gases, but they are susceptible to electromagnetic forces as well.

Plasma Dynamics

The early researches into the nature of plasmas, from the glow-discharge tubes to the Kennelly–Heaviside layer, dealt essentially with plasmas at rest. When World War II ended, many physicists turned their attention to the nature of plasmas in motion. This study is called *plasma dynamics,* and forms the subject matter for the rest of this book.

Like the first phase of plasma research, plasma dynamics offers engineering applications that are truly exciting, and chapters 5 through 7 will examine a few of these.

But it was actually studies of the heavens that first attracted interest in plasma dynamics. For, during the latter 1930's and war-torn '40's, astronomers and physicists began to realize that the universe—the stars and nebulas and galaxies of infinite space—are made almost entirely of plasma. From the ionosphere a hundred kilometers or so over our heads, out to the deepest reaches of the cosmos, plasma is by far the most common form of matter.

Far from being an unusual state, plasma is the major constituent of the universe. It's only in small, cold, out-of-the way minor planets, such as ours, that the less-energetic states of matter can exist!

THREE

The Birth and Death of Stars

Most of the universe is plasma.

The sun is a sphere of plasma a million kilometers wide. And the sun is merely a middling-small star, as stars go. There some 100 billion (10^{11}) stars in our own Milky Way galaxy, with enough free gas floating in interstellar space to build billions more. Much of this gas is ionized, and therefore is plasma. The sun sits off at one edge of the Milky Way galaxy, some 30,000 light years from the galactic core. And the Milky Way is only one out of hundreds of billions of galaxies.

As astronomers began to realize that the universe is mostly plasma, they also came to the conclusion that plasma physics might help to explain many of the unanswered questions about how stars are created, and how they die out. Plasma physicists began making important contributions to astronomy and cosmology in the 1950's.

Then, in the 1960's, startling discoveries burst upon the astronomers. Quasars and pulsars, exploding galaxies and disappearing stars all clamored for explanation. In all of these exciting and strange new phenomena, plasma physics plays a key role. For there are cataclysms exploding in the heavens of a violence undreamed of even a few short years ago. And only plasmas are energetic enough to undergo such shattering catastrophes.

To understand what's happening in the heavens—to understand

A SPIRAL GALAXY *seen in the consellation Ursa Major. Called M81, this galaxy is somewhat like our own Milky Way galaxy of some 10^{11} stars. Our solar system is located in one of the spiral arms of the Milky Way galaxy. (Mt. Wilson and Mt. Palomar Observatories)*

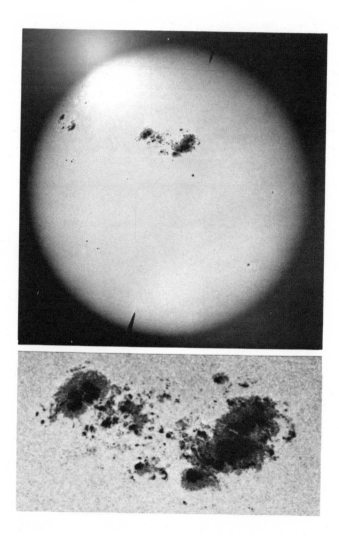

THE SPOTTED SUN. *Sunspots were first observed in Galileo's time, but no completely satisfactory explanation of them has yet been found. Solar flares—powerful explosions on the sun—come from sunspot areas. Notice that the sunspots seem to show a structure something like that of iron filings scattered around a magnet. (Mt. Wilson and Mt. Palomar Observatories)*

how our own sun and Earth were born and how they will die—we must understand plasma physics.

The Sun as a Plasma Generator

In a very real sense, all life on Earth depends on plasma energy, since the sun is a plasma energy generator.

The first inkling that plasmas might exist in space came in the 1850's. While Crookes was working with glow discharges, astronomers began to realize that there was a link between flares on the sun and sudden disruptions of the Earth's magnetic field.

A solar flare is the most violent event in the solar system. It's an explosion on the sun that's equal to the force of 10^{10} *megatons* of TNT exploding. While this is stupendous on the human scale, we'll soon see that it's only a tiny fraction of the sun's available energy. In the next chapter we'll take a closer look at solar flares and the violent effects they have on Earth's magnetic field. For the moment, our interest is mainly historical: astronomers found that within hours after a flare erupted on the sun, the Earth's magnetic field buckled and quivered as if it had been hit by some titanic force. There was no direct proof, but the circumstantial evidence certainly pointed to a link between flares on the sun and the magnetic disturbances on Earth.

In 1878 there was a total eclipse of the sun, and astronomers from all over the world photographed the event. When the main body of the sun is hidden by the Moon's disk, it's possible to see the *corona*, a wispy, tenuous crown of plasma that surrounds the sun. The corona is too faint to be seen except during an eclipse, since its pearly-white glow is ordinarily drowned out completely by the sun's fierce glow.

The photographs of the 1878 eclipse showed that the corona isn't just a featureless haze of light. It definitely showed streamers, curved filaments, near the sun's north and south poles. The corona's structure strongly resembled the kind of pattern that iron filings make when sprinkled over a magnet. Could the sun be a magnet?

In 1908 the American astronomer George Ellery Hale (1868–

A BUTTERFLY OF LIGHT, *this beautiful photograph of the sun's corona was taken during the total eclipse of March 7, 1970 in Yuatepec, Mexico, by a team from the High Altitude Observatory of Boulder, Colorado, led by Dr. Gordon Newkirk, Jr. The corona is shaped by the sun's general magnetic field.*

1938) showed that there are strong magnetic fields in and around sunspots.

Sunspots had been observed and puzzled over since Galileo first pointed a telescope toward the sun. The sun has no solid surface, but a shining layer of plasma called the *photosphere* (sphere of light). The photosphere's temperature is some 6000°K, hot enough to vaporize any material known to man, and to ionize the gases present there. Above the photosphere is a transparent band of plasma called the *chromosphere* (sphere of color) which, during an eclipse, can be seen giving off a reddish glow. Above the chromosphere is the corona.

The sunspots are dark whirlpools, thousands of kilometers across, set into the shining photosphere. They appear and disappear, with individual spots lasting anywhere from a few days to a few weeks. There is apparently an 11-year cycle to sunspot activity; that is, every 11 years or so (the cycle is not precise) the number of sunspots will reach a maximum and then for the next five or six years will taper off to a minimum number. Then the cycle begins anew. Solar flares are associated with sunspots, as we'll see in the next chapter.

Hale found that there are intense magnetic fields around the sunspots, field of several thousand gauss or more. In contrast, Earth's magnetic field is less than one gauss, and that's strong enough to keep compass needles aligned roughly north–south all across the planet. Man-made electrical magnets have achieved fields of 100,000 gauss and even more, but not over the thousands of kilometers of a typical sunspot.

In 1913 Hale announced that the sun also has a general magnetic field, independent of the sunspots, with a north and south magnetic pole like the Earth's magnetic poles. This general field is responsible for the filamentary structure seen in the corona. It apparently varies between a few gauss and a hundred gauss or so. And it switches polarity! The north and south poles flip positions, presumably in the same 11-odd-year cycle as the sunspots.

These discoveries of Hale's, and the work of other astrophysicists who followed him, showed that there are enormous energies locked in the sun's seething plasmas. Moreover, the sun is beaming out the

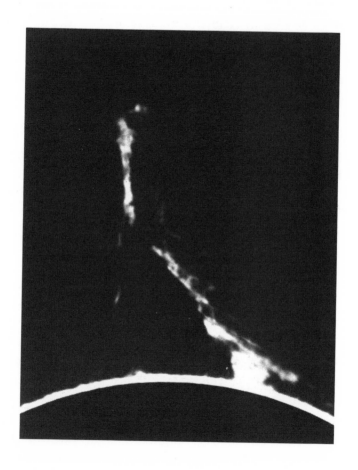

SOLAR PROMINENCE *of glowing hydrogen plasma is hurled hundreds of thousands of kilometers out into space. Such prominences are quite ordinary events on the sun. (Mt. Wilson and Mt. Palomar Observatories)*

electromagnetic energy we call sunshine at a rate of 3.8×10^{33} ergs per second. An *erg* is a tiny unit of energy. A fifty-watt lamp radiates half a billion (0.5×10^9) ergs per second. It takes 10^{10} ergs to equal one kilowatt. But 10^{33} is a huge number. The sun's output of energy is equal to the explosive energy of 3.8×10^{10} megatons of TNT. Every second.

What's more, the sun has been radiating energy at this rate for billions of years. By the 1930's, it became clear that the sun has been in existence for at least four billion years. Where could all that energy come from?

What makes the sun shine?

You recall that the plasma physicists and nuclear physicists parted ways around the turn of the century, in Rutherford's time. In the latter part of the 1930's they joined forces again, this time to tackle the basic question of what makes the sun and stars shine.

The sun is 1.39 million kilometers in diameter. Its mass is 2×10^{27} metric tons, some 330,000 times more massive than our fairly sizable planet. It is composed almost completely of hydrogen and helium, the two lightest elements, with slightly less than one percent of heavier elements. The photosphere temperature, as we've seen, is 6000°K; calculations show that the temperature at the sun's core must reach an inconceivable 20 million degrees Kelvin.

If the sun were a mixture of pure carbon and oxygen and burned like a coal flame, its 2×10^{27} tons would have been consumed within a few thousand years. If the sun were slowly shrinking and converting gravitational energy into heat and light, it would run out of energy in a few million years, at most.

By the mid-1930's, it was clear that the sun must be plasma throughout. Deep inside the sun's core, at temperatures of millions of degrees, the plasma must be completely ionized. The atomic nuclei are stripped bare of orbital electrons, all the atoms are ionized fully, and they have enormous energy invested in them.

Using this picture of the sun's interior, two men added a knowledge of nuclear physics to explain the source of the sun's energy. Hans Bethe (born 1906), who had come to America from Germany, and Karl F. von Weizsacker (born 1912), in Germany, worked independently of each other. In 1938, they both showed that the sun is a nuclear furnace. It is constantly converting hydrogen nuclei into helium nuclei, at the rate of four to one. This process is called *thermonuclear fusion.* In the fusion process, each helium nucleus that's produced is 0.7 percent lighter than the four hydrogen nuclei that were originally present. That 0.7 percent of the original mass is converted into energy, the energy we call sunshine.

TABLE 3-1: SOLAR AND STELLAR HYDROGEN FUSION PROCESSES

Carbon Chain

$$H^1 + C^{12} \rightarrow N^{13} + \gamma$$
$$N^{13} \rightarrow C^{13} + e^+ + v$$
$$C^{13} + H^1 \rightarrow N^{14} + \gamma$$
$$N^{14} + H^1 \rightarrow O^{15} + \gamma$$
$$O^{15} \rightarrow N^{15} + e^+ + v$$
$$N^{15} + H^1 \rightarrow C^{12} + He^4$$

Proton-Proton Reaction

$$H^1 + H^1 \rightarrow H^2 + e + v$$
$$H^2 + H^1 \rightarrow He^3 + \gamma$$
$$He^3 + He^3 \rightarrow He^4 + 2H^1$$

Key

H^1 = Hydrogen (proton)
H^2 = Deuterium (deuteron)
He^3, He^4 = Helium isotopes
C^{12}, C^{13} = Carbon isotopes
N^{13}, N^{14} = Nitrogen isotopes
O^{15} = Oxygen isotope
e^+ = positron (positive electron)
γ = gamma ray
v = neutrino

Two nuclear fusion processes for converting hydrogen to helium, releasing energy in the form of gamma rays and neutrinos. Note that in the carbon chain, only four hydrogen nuclei (protons) and one carbon nucleus are required as input; the carbon nucleus after several transmutations returns to its original form at the chain's end. In the sun, the proton-proton reaction produces most of the energy. Carbon chain reactions are more important in hotter stars.

The sun is continuously changing its hydrogen into helium, through thermonuclear fusion reactions. Every second, some four million tons of matter disappear from the sun, converted into energy and radiated away into space. This has been going on for at least four billion years, and the sun is so huge that it can continue to throw away mass like this for another five to ten billion years, easily. And when all its hydrogen is changed into helium, the sun will be only 0.7 percent lighter than it would be if it were entirely made of hydrogen.

Thermonuclear fusion is the process that makes the stars shine. All life on Earth depends on the thermonuclear reactions going on in the sun. As we'll see in Chapter 7, one of the brightest hopes of plasma physicists is to produce controlled thermonuclear reactors here on Earth, so that all man's energy needs can be generated from the hydrogen of the oceans. Of course, we already have a sort of uncontrolled thermonuclear reactor in our hands: the hydrogen bomb.

The conclusion that the sun's energy comes from nuclear reactions was a landmark achievement. In 1967 Bethe was awarded a Nobel Prize in physics for this work. Remember, in 1938 nuclear power was a dream shared only by a handful of physicists and science-fiction writers. The discovery that the sun and stars were nuclear reactors helped to spur the physicists and engineers down the road to nuclear power. And bombs.

Origin of the Solar System

In many ways, the sun is a very ordinary star. The one main exception is that it's the only star we know of that has planets orbiting around it. Astronomers have deduced the presence of planets circling other stars, from indirect evidence. But no one has actually seen such planets. The other stars are simply too far away to allow us to observe a faint, small planet directly.

In trying to explain the origin of the solar system, we're also attempting to learn something about the rest of the universe. For if we can show that our solar system came about as the result of a natural sequence of events, then we can expect many other stars to have planets. But if the solar system is the result of some rare, perhaps unique, occurrence, then we can't expect other stars to have planetary systems.

There've been many theories about the solar system's origin. None of them has satisfied all the questions that can be asked. But as we'll see, with the help of plasma physics we can at least sketch in the broad outline of how the solar system was created. Without plasma physics, not even that much could be done satisfactorily.

The main problem with most of the theories is simply that the solar system is a wild congregation of bodies.

Sizes range from the sun's 1.39-million-kilometer diameter down to dust particles of about 10^{-5} centimeter. The sun contains 99% of all the mass of the solar system, yet has only about one percent of the system's angular momentum, or spin energy. All the planets lie in almost the same flat plane, but not quite. Four of the planets seem to be giant-sized ice balls, four of them are smaller chunks of rock and metal, and the remaining one—Pluto—is a frozen question mark.

One planet has rings around it. Why only one? Why any at all? Next to Jupiter, the largest planet, is a zone of tiny fragments called the asteroid belt (or, more correctly, the planetoid belt). Uranus rolls along on its back, its pole pointed toward the sun, instead of standing reasonably upright on its axis as the other planets do. Venus is covered with clouds and rotates in a direction opposite to that of all the other planets. Earth is brimful of water, but no other planet shows a trace of liquid water on its surface. The Moon has a density completely different from Earth's, yet the Earth–Moon system comes closer to being a double planet rather than a typical planet–satellite combination.

The wonder of it all isn't that so many theories have been tried and found wanting. The amazing thing is that scientists still try! If man has one trait that goes deeper than his curiosity, it must be his stubborness.

All the theories that have been proposed to explain the solar system can be classified as either evolutionary or revolutionary. The evolutionary type of explanation sees the formation of the solar system as a natural sequence of events, perhaps even an inevitable consequence of the birth of a star. In contrast, the revolutionary theories picture the solar system as being formed as the result of some special occasion, a cataclysm or a special act of creation. For example, most early religions considered the Earth to be so unique that it took a special act of the gods to create it. The ancients thought of the Earth as being the center of the universe, literally.

TABLE 3-2: GENERAL FEATURES OF THE SOLAR SYSTEM

Planet	Diameter (Kilometers)	Mean Radius of Orbit (10⁶ Kilometers)	(AU's)	Spin Rate	Orbital Period	Density (times H_2O)	Mass (Earth=1)	Inclination of Poles to Earth's	Inclination of Orbit Relative to Earth's
MERCURY	4,960	58	0.39	58.5d	88d	3.8	0.06	?	7°
VENUS	12,320	107	0.72	116d	225d	5.0	0.82	?	3°23'
EARTH	12,673	149	1.00	24+h	365.25d	5.52	1.00	23°27'	....
MOON	3,356	......	......	29.5d	29.5d (geo-centric)	3.37	0.012	....	....
MARS	6,720	226	1.52	24h37m	~2y	3.81	0.11	25°12'	1°51'
PLANETOIDS	......	394 (avg.)	2.65	......	......	......	......	....	....
JUPITER	141,920	773	5.20	9h55m	~12y	1.36	318.36	3°7'	1°18'
SATURN	120,160	1,418	9.55	10h38m	~30y	0.72	95.22	26°45'	2°29'
URANUS	49,410	2,853	19.22	10.7h	~84y	1.27	14.58	98°	0°46'
NEPTUNE	52,800	4,668	30.11	15.8h	~165y	1.20	17.26	29°	1°46'
PLUTO	5,760 (?)	5,866	39.60	?	~250y	1.0 (!?)	1.0 (?)	?	17°7'

The first attempt at a scientific explanation for the solar system's origin was put forth about 200 years ago by the German philosopher Immanuel Kant (1724–1804) and elaborated upon by the French astronomer Pierre Simon de Laplace (1749–1827). This was the *nebular hypothesis.* Kant and Laplace suggested that the planets originated in a gas cloud—a nebula—surrounding the sun. The gas condensed to form the planets and other solid bodies of the solar system. This was put forth as a natural-sequence, evolutionary type of theory. There was no reason why similar events shouldn't occur on other stars.

The sharp edge of mathematical fact burst this theoretical balloon about a century later. Maxwell, truly a giant of mathematical physics, showed on paper that a gas cloud simply wouldn't behave the way Kant and Laplace wanted it to. If all the material now contained in the solid bodies of the solar system—planets, satellites, meteoroids, and so on—was originally gaseous, the gas cloud would have been very thin. These solid bodies amount to little more than a thousandth of the sun's present mass. A gas cloud of that mass, Maxwell showed, would not have condensed to form solid bodies. The kinetic theory of gases predicted that it would have dispersed, wafted away into space.

Remember, these men were thinking in terms of gases, not plasmas. We'll look at their theories as they themselves presented them and not consider plasma physics until it was actually brought into the picture, in the mid-twentieth century.

The nebular hypothesis collapsed under the impact of Maxwell's rigorous logic. Toward the end of the nineteenth century, a new theory took its place: a revolutionary type of theory. This was the *stellar-encounter* concept, expressed in the twentieth century by the British astrophysicists Sir James Jeans (1877–1946) and Sir Harold Jeffreys (born 1891), and the Americans Thomas Chrowder Chamberlain (1843–1928) and Forest Ray Moulton (1872–1952).

Reduced to its simplest terms, the stellar-encounter theory pictures a star passing close enough to the sun to pull out a filament of gaseous material, due to the immense gravitational tides raised by such a close encounter. The gas filament then condensed to form the planets, satellites, and the rest. Since the stars are ordinarily separated by light years of distance, such a close encounter would be a very, *very* rare event. If this was the way the planets were formed, then planetary systems must be extremely few in number. Perhaps ours is unique.

Even at the highest tide of its popularity, many scientists regarded the stellar-encounter theory with misgivings. For one thing, why should our solar system be unique? Ever since Copernicus showed that the Earth isn't the center of the universe, astronomers have tended to worry about any theory that makes our particular place in the world special or unique.

Then too, a filament of gases pulled from the sun's interior would be no more likely to condense into planets than the Kant–Laplace nebula. Jeans and his followers tried to counter that argument. They showed that the filament could have been very massive, much more massive than the solid bodies of today's solar system. Mathematical analysis showed that if the gas was massive enough, solid planets could condense out of it. But then, what happened to the extra gas, the material that didn't go into building solid bodies?

Also, even though the gas filament might have been very massive, it would also have been very hot, coming from the sun's interior. Its high temperature would have made it tend to disperse, not contract, thereby counteracting the massiveness argument.

There were two other stumbling blocks. One: the sun is composed mainly of hydrogen and helium. The planets have very different chemical compositions. If the material for the planets was pulled out of the sun, why don't the planets have similar makeups? And two: the sun is spinning very slowly, once in about 27 days (different parts of the sun spin at different rates, showing that it can't be solid or liquid). The planets, in their wide-swinging orbits, have almost all of the solar system's angular momentum, or spin energy. If the planets had been yanked out of the sun, the action should have forced the sun to spin much faster than it does now. Either the stellar-encounter theory is wrong, or something slowed down the sun's spin rate.

By 1950, astronomers and astrophysicists had come across two new tools to help them explain the origin of the solar system. One: the 200-inch telescope at Mt. Palomar (named after Hale) was helping to show star-building activities deep in space; and two: plasma physicists had turned their attention to the dynamics of plasmas and their interactions with magnetic fields.

The new theory they built up is often called the *dust-cloud* theory. In some ways it harks back to the old nebular hypothesis. But there are very important differences.

The dust-cloud theory envisions the birth of the entire solar system—sun, planets and all—as happening together, all at the same time. It's an evolutionary theory, in that it sees the development of a planetary system as part of the natural evolution of a young star.

"Dust," in astronomical jargon, means tiny grains of solid matter, usually a fraction of a centimeter across. The dust grains seen in huge clouds out among the stars are apparently composed mainly of hydrogen that's frozen solid, with perhaps other elements mixed in.

An extremely important contribution to the dust-cloud theory was the realization that stars are "nuclear cookers." That is, the nuclear reactions in the stars "cook" constantly-heavier elements. Young stars convert hydrogen into helium. As a star gets older, it begins to convert the helium into carbon, oxygen and other elements. All the elements we know of, except hydrogen, have been "cooked" inside stars that are much older than the sun. Where the hydrogen came from originally is a mystery that cosmologists have argued without success for generations.

Stars are born in vast clouds of dust, and they are often born in clusters of many stars. In time, the cluster breaks apart and the stars are more or less alone. Stars also die, after they've used all their available nuclear fuel. Frequently their death throes are marked by titanic explosions in which much of the star's material is hurled back into space. This material—enriched now with heavy elements—mixes with the interstellar gases and plasmas to form the building matter for new stars.

The sun is four to five billion years old. There are many stars twice that age in our galaxy. So it's reasonable to believe that the sun's original building material was not merely hydrogen, but contained some helium and heavier elements, as well.

Astronomers have seen the birth of new stars. Star-building re-

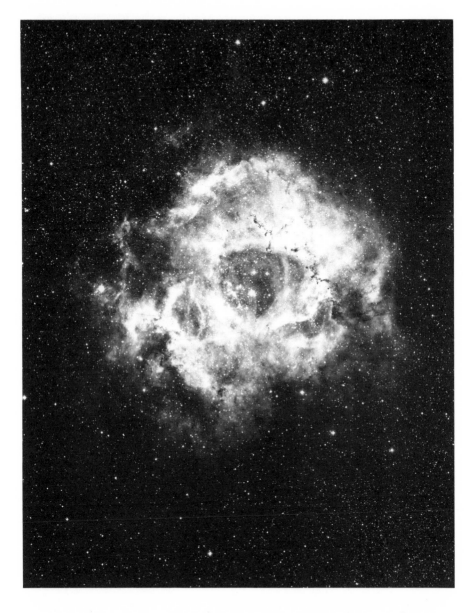

STARS IN THE MAKING. *Dark globules of interstellar dust seen here in the Rosette Nebula are forming protostars, which will eventually become new stars. The glowing plasma is being blown away from the center of the nebula by radiation pressure coming from hot, young blue stars there. (Mt. Wilson and Mt. Palomar Observatories)*

gions of the Milky Way are rich mixtures of bright, glowing plasma and dark clumps of cool gas and dust. The stars begin their lives as huge globules of dust, a light year or more in diameter. Astronomers call these globules *protostars.*

Our solar system began as such a vast cloud of gas and dust. The original cloud was considerably more massive than the sun is today, at least 20% more massive. The original temperature of the dust cloud may have been quite low, about $50°K$ ($-370°F$); this is the approximate temperature for any nonluminous body in deep space, far from a warming star.

The dust grains in the cloud probably consisted mainly of hydrogen and hydrogen compounds, such as water (H_2O), ammonia (NH_3) and methane (CH_4). We can call such grains *ices.* There must have also been grains of heavier materials, silicates and metals, which are called *earthy* particles.

Two more ingredients are needed to complete the picture. The cloud was rotating, and it was permeated by a weak magnetic field.

There's no exact explanation of how the rotation began, but it would be difficult to prevent a cloud of that size from rotating, especially when it's being influenced by the small but real gravitational effects of distant stars. Likewise, there's no specific answer as to where the magnetic field came from. It was, at the outset, probably no more than 10^{-5} gauss. There appears to be such a weak magnetic field throughout the entire Milky Way galaxy. Perhaps our cloud merely shared in this general field.

As the cloud rotated, it contracted. Simple physics tells us that much. As it shrank, its density and central temperature had to increase. And the magnetic field became constantly stronger as the cloud condensed. The magnetic field was stretched over a light year's diameter originally. As the cloud shrank, the field shrank with it and became more concentrated, more intense, stronger. The same amount of electromagnetic energy was being concentrated into a smaller volume.

The cloud's contraction quickly turned into a collapse. The cloud fell in on itself, converting gravitational energy into heat. In just a few million years (an eyeblink in astronomy) the dark dust cloud turned into a glowing sphere of plasma, a brilliant new star.

Our newly-born sun was glowing from gravitational energy, and still collapsing. And it was spinning very rapidly, a revolution every few hours. All the angular momentum from the original light-year-wide cloud was still contained by the sun, and the farther it shrank, the faster it spun.

Picture how things looked when the sun had shrunk down to the size of Mercury's present orbit, roughly 40 times the size of the sun today.

The sun's surface was indistinct; such young stars often pulsate irregularly, heaving with new energies. There was a vast cloud of dust and plasma around the sun, and the cloud was also spinning rapidly. So rapidly, in fact, that the cloud soon flattened out into a disk around the sun's equator. The disk was huge, extending far out into space. It was at least ten times more massive than all the solid bodies in the solar system today, and possibly 100 times more massive. And much of this disk was plasma, not gas, since the sun's heat radiation ionized the gas in the disk out to a considerable distance.

The sun's temperature was also high enough to vaporize the dust grains—ices and earthy particles alike—through much of the disk. Vaporize them, but not dissociate them. That is, compounds such as water, ammonia, and so on were still present in the vapor phase. If and when the temperature dropped sufficiently, they could recondense into solid grains.

And the temperature in the disk did drop, fairly quickly. For the disk was wide and flat; it had a large surface area compared to its total volume. It could, and did, radiate away much of its heat, passed it out into space. Take a look at any radiator: it's built to have a maximum of surface area compared to its volume.

As the temperature in the disk dropped, the dust grains could recondense. Now several things began to happen at once. The grains started clumping together, beginning the process that eventually built up the planets. Most of the disk material—which was 10 to 100 times more massive than the planets, etc.—was pushed out of the solar system. And the sun's spin rate slowed down from a revolution every few hours to one revolution in about a month.

None of this could have happened unless the sun and the disk were plasma. As long as the theoreticians considered the sun as gaseous rather than plasma, there could be no way of explaining how the solar system went from a fast-spinning sun and a surrounding gas cloud to a family of solid planets and a slow-spinning sun.

The infant sun and its surrounding disk were plasma, and could be shaped, molded by a magnetic field. There was a magnetic field present, the field that had been in the original dust cloud. That magnetic field is still present in interplanetary space; it's been measured by many satellites and space probes.

Now we must visualize the invisible. Magnetic lines of force can be thought of as something like rubber bands that are infinitely thin and almost infinitely pliable. In the early solar system, we can picture magnetic field lines looping out from the sun and through the wide, flat disk, like rubber bands that have been stretched very far. The magnetic field would be much stronger within the plasma of the sun and disk than in the relatively empty space outside the plasma, just as the magnetic field in a metal magnet is stronger than the field outside of it.

The Swedish physicist Hannes Alfvén (born 1908) pointed out in the early 1950's that this magnetic field was the mechanism that both slowed down the sun's rotation and expelled much of the disk material from the solar system. And it even indirectly guided the formation of the planets. (In 1970 Alfvén won a Nobel Prize for this work.) Interactions of a plasma with a magnetic field are called *magnetohydrodynamic* interactions. Magnetohydrodynamics is usually abbreviated, mercifully, to MHD.

The sun was spinning once every few hours, and the plasma disk was trying to keep up with it. If the magnetic field lines in the disk were perfectly rigid, like the spokes of a wheel, they would have held the plasma disk to the sun's rotation rate.

But magnetic field lines aren't rigid; they're very pliable. As the sun rotated, the field lines twisted and looped, more like rubber bands than the spokes of a wheel. The net effect, Alfvén showed, was that the MHD forces tended to make the disk plasma speed up, but at the expense of the sun's angular momentum. The sun slowed down. Calculations have shown that in as little as a million years the sun could have slowed to its present spin rate, thanks to "magnetic braking."

As the same time, these same MHD forces were pushing the plasma disk further and further away from the sun. Much of the disk material was eventually swept entirely out of the solar system by MHD forces.

And the planet-building processes were also greatly influenced by the magnetic field.

The plasma disk was rotating, gaining angular momentum steadily and being pushed away from the sun. And we've seen that it was cooling rather quickly, too. Under such conditions, the plasma in the disk would be whipped into a state of constant agitation, a turbulent froth, streaked with eddies and whirlpools. Von Weizsacker first suggested that these eddies might be places where the disk material would tend to come together and begin building large solid bodies.

But what were the available building materials? Close to the sun, the disk temperature was too high to allow the icy grains to recondense. The earthy particles could solidify, though, and apparently formed the basic building blocks for the four inner planets —Mercury, Venus, Earth and Mars. Farther away, the ices could condense, and since they were far more abundant than the earthy grains, the farther planets could become huge. Jupiter, Saturn, Uranus and Neptune are giant ice planets.

The exact mechanics of sticking together billions of dust grains to form even a small planet are far from understood. The process is called *aggregation,* and at this level of our knowledge, aggregation is little more than a name and a hope. But there's some evidence that this is actually the way the planets were formed. Some meteorites have been found to be composed of tiny globular pieces, called *chondrules.* The chondrules are very much what you would expect to find in a small body that's been formed by the aggregation of tiny grains. In a body the size of the Earth, or even the Moon, such evidence of aggregation becomes obliterated under the sheer weight of billions of tons of matter.

The inner planets, then, are small and dense, built out of the silicates and metals of the earthy grains. Venus and Eath were apparently in the middle of the earthy grain belt, and are the largest of the inner planets. Closer to the sun, even the earthy grains were probably kept vaporized. Farther away, the earthy materials might not have been so abundant, for Mars is quite small, and beyond Mars is the planetoid belt. This swarm of mini-planets certainly gives the appearance of being a region where the supply of earthy materials simply ran too low to build a respectable planet. Of course, the gravitational influence of Jupiter might have helped to prevent such a planet from being formed.

Jupiter and Saturn are the largest of the giant planets. Apparently they were able to pull in, gravitationally, a considerable amount of gaseous or plasma hydrogen and helium directly from the disk. Uranus and Neptune, farther away from the sun, somehow didn't get as much disk vapor for themselves. There are several theoretical explanations for this, none of them wholly satisfactory.

Distant Pluto, out on the edges of the observable solar system, is almost a complete question mark. Not enough is known about it to say anything except that it might have originally been a moon of Neptune that somehow broke away and established itself in a planetary orbit.

While the planets were building and most of the material in the plasma disk was being pushed out of the solar system by MHD forces, the sun turned into a true nuclear furnace. The density and temperature at the sun's core reached the point where thermonuclear reactions were ignited, and the sun started converting hydrogen into helium and energy. The sun's gravitational collapse stopped, counteracted by the enormous gas pressures pushing up from the core.

There are still many unanswered questions about the solar system's origin. But thanks to Bethe, von Weizsacker, Alfvén and many others, we can now understand in outline how a distended cloud of dust could form the sun and planets we know today. It could only happen in a plasma; MHD forces shaped the solar system.

Is there any real evidence that things actually happened this way? Or is the theory merely an attempt to match an explanation to the observed features of today's solar system?

One critical point of the dust-cloud theory is the use of MHD forces to slow the sun's rotation and expel the "extra" material from the planet-building disk. There is evidence, circumstantial but important, to support the MHD slowdown concept. The evidence comes from the stars.

Astronomers classify the stars by letters that denote their temperature range, starting with O for the hottest stars and going down to class M for the coolest. There are a few other classes for peculiar stars, but they needn't bother us now. The classification sequence started about a century ago, and was originally a very orderly system, with A stars the hottest and so on down the alphabet. But as astronomical instruments and techniques improved, astronomers found that B stars were hotter than A stars, new types were found and new letters attached to them, old types were elimated from the system. In short, chaos threatened the system of stellar classifications.

The system now reads, from hottest to coolest, O, B, A, F, G, K, M. You can easily remember it the way astronomers do, by memorizing, "Oh be a fine girl, kiss me!"

Each class is divided into ten subclasses, which are indicated by numbers. Thus, the sun is a G2 star, slightly cooler than Capella, which is a G0, although both are yellow stars. Blue Rigel is B8, red Betelgeuse is M2.

A star's temperature is a good indication of its age. In general, the hottest stars—O, B, and A—are the youngest. All the stars are spinning, and astronomers can measure a star's spin rate.

When the spin rates of thousands of stars are compared, a staggering fact comes leaping out of the numbers: the hot young stars are whizzing away at velocities up to 500 kilometers per second, while the cooler, older G, K and M stars seldom rotate faster than 5 kilometers per second.

It looks very much as if the younger O, B and A stars haven't been in existence long enough to allow MHD braking to slow their spin rates. Older stars, such as the sun, appear to have had their angular momentum absorbed by the planetary disk and the solid bodies of the solar system.

TABLE 3-3: STELLAR CLASSES AND SPIN RATES

Class	Stable Life Span (Years)	Color	Maximum Rotation Rate (km/sec)
Oe, Be*	———	blue, violet	500
O, B	8 to 400 million	blue, violet	250
A	400 million to 4 billion	blue-white, white	250
F0 to F2	4 to 10 billion	white	250
F5 to F8	4 to 10 billion	white	70
G	10 to 30 billion	yellow	5
K	30 to 70 billion	orange	5
M	more than 70 billion	red	5

*Unusual and very rare types of stars

We can extend this admittedly circumstantial evidence to consider two more possibilities. First, if we can believe that MHD forces have slowed the sun's spin rate, then we can agree that the same forces must have expelled the "extra" disk material after (or even during) the formation of the planets. Second—and even more exciting—if those older stars are *all* spinning slowly because of MHD braking, there must be an excellent chance that most of them have their own planetary systems. Thus the dust-cloud theory not only explains the formation of our solar system, it predicts the existence of planets around most of the stars in the universe!

Because the universe is indeed mainly plasma, we find that plasma physics not only helps us to understand the birth of stars and solar systems, it also helps us to understand how stars die, and the titanic explosions of stars that are called *supernovas.*

There was a supernova explosion in the Milky Way galaxy some 6000 years ago, when man's highest civilization was a scattering of farming villages, twenty centuries before the Egyptians started building their pyramids. There have been other supernovas in our galaxy since then, but let's focus our attention on this one.

The star that exploded was a massive one, more than twice the sun's size. Even so, it might have had a planetary system around it. If it did, any life on those planets was utterly destroyed when the star exploded.

For thousands of years the glaring light of that supernova expanded across space. Finally, in the year 1054 AD (on July 4 of all days) the light reached Earth. Chinese and Japanese astronomers suddenly saw a new star in the sky, where no star had been before. And it was bright enough to be seen in full daylight! They recorded this strange event in their annals. American Indians in the southwestern desert of the United States also noticed the new star, which first appeared near the crescent moon, and drew pictures on rocks of the fearsome change in the sky. If anyone in Europe noticed the new star, no enduring record of the discovery was made. Europe was in the depths of a Dark Age; the First Crusade was still nearly half a century in the future.

The Europeans later came to dominate astronomy and all of modern science. The very word *nova* comes from Latin and originally meant a "new" star—one that suddenly appeared where the naked eye could see no star before. Modern astronomers use the term "nova" to describe a certain type of stellar explosion. A supernova is a much more violent explosion, and usually signals the death of the star. In a supernova explosion, the star will release as much energy in 24 hours as the sun gives off in a billion years!

In 1731 a British physician and amateur astronomer, John Bevis,

THE CRAB NEBULA, *in the constellation Scorpio, is the remains of a supernova explosion that was first observed by Asian astronomers in 1054 AD, when the "new star" was so bright that it could be seen in full daylight. At the heart of the Crab Nebula is a tiny, ultra-dense pulsar. The Crab Nebula is a source of strong radio wave and x-ray emissions. Its plasma clouds are expanding through space at a velocity of more than 1000 kilometers per second. (Mt. Wilson and Mt. Palomar Observatories)*

happened to point his telescope toward the constellation Taurus, the Bull. Among the stars in that region he saw a faint, fuzzy patch of light. Astronomers call anything that can't be put into a definite category a *nebula*, meaning a cloud. In most cases, the nebula turns out to be a star cluster or a galaxy or a comet. But often a nebula is actually a cloud of gas or plasma out among the stars.

In the nineteenth century Bevis' nebula was observed and even photographed. It became known as the Crab Nebula, because of its shape. By the twentieth century, measurements showed that the nebula was expanding: its gases (later found to be plasmas) were spreading through space at more than 1000 kilometers per second.

The astronomers concluded that the Crab Nebula is indeed the remains of the supernova of 1054. It was once a massive star. But as the star's nuclear fuel became exhausted, the star collapsed and then exploded. Such a fate may await the sun, although modern theory predicts that if the sun explodes it will be a milder, nova-type explosion. The sun won't wreck itself, but will merely blow off its outer layers of plasma and then settle back to become a dwarf star. Eventually it will cool off and go dark. Scant comfort to us. Even a "mild" nova blast will boil away our atmosphere and oceans. But at least there seems to be five to ten billion years ahead of us before the sun starts to run low on nuclear fuel.

Shortly after World War II astronomers discovered that the Crab Nebula emits radio waves. Radio astronomy had been born in the early 1930's, but was held in abeyance during the war. By the late 1940's, though, war-motivated improvements in electronics and plasma physics combined to make radio astronomy an enormously active and exciting branch of research. The radio astronomers quickly found that there are vast clouds of gas in interstellar space, so thin that they're invisible to optical telescopes. But they emit radio waves. There also seemed to be strong radio emissions coming from distinct spots in the sky, but very few of these radio sources could be identified with anything visible to optical telescopes.

The Crab Nebula was the first radio source to be identified with an optically visible object. It was emitting radio waves just as naturally as it emits light. Or was it "just as naturally?"

If you heat an object to a sufficiently high temperature, it will begin to radiate electromagnetic waves. Some of this electromagnetic energy will be at the wavelengths we call visible light. The object will glow. But some of the energy will also be at other wavelengths. A small part of it will be at radio frequencies. For more than a century, astronomers have been able to determine the temperature of a star by analyzing its visible light. Radio astronomers tried to use the same technique on the Crab Nebula's radio emission. They came up with a temperature of some 2,000,000°K, which was far in excess of the temperature deduced from visible light measurements.

There was no doubt about the optical measurements, so the radio measurement had to be wrong. *Or*—the radio energy given off by the Crab Nebula wasn't due to simple temperature effects. Could there be a *non-thermal* cause for the Crab's radio emission?

Up to this point in time, all the energy processes associated with stars had been assumed to be strictly thermal in origin. That is, the electromagnetic energy given off by a star was thought to be caused directly by simple thermal effects: the hotter the body, the more intense its energy output.

The Russian astrophysicist I. S. Shklovsky suggested that the Crab Nebula's radio and light output might be due to non-thermal plasma processes. He pointed out that the Nebula is a cloud of plasma that is probably laced with a strong magnetic field. Under these conditions, the free electrons in the plasma would be accelerated by energy imparted to them by the magnetic field. Such electron acceleration is seen in man-made *synchrotrons*. The synchrotron is a device developed by nuclear physicists specifically to accelerate particles to very high velocities, for use in nuclear physics experiments. Shklovsky said that the Crab Nebula might be a natural synchrotron, where the electrons were radiating radio energy as a result of being accelerated by the plasma's magnetic field.

The suggestion was subject to an easy test. Man-made synchrotrons also emit light, but their light is heavily polarized. That is, the electromagnetic waves of the visible light are aligned along a preferred direction. If you look at an ordinary light source through a Polaroid filter, you can rotate the filter in any direction and the light will appear unchanged. But if the light is polarized, then as you rotate the filter you will cut off more and more of the light until it becomes completely blanked out.

Astronomers quickly found that the Crab Nebula's light and radio output are both heavily polarized. This proved Shklovsky's synchrotron idea. But it raised another problem: what's providing the energy to drive these synchrotron reactions?

Apparently something in the Crab Nebula is producing enough energy continuously to make the entire Nebula—which is six light years across—behave like a gigantic electron accelerator. The fastest electrons are emitting visible light; the slower ones are putting out radio waves. But what's the energy source? It can't be the supernova explosion itself: that energy was expended centuries ago. To prove this point, there have been at least two more recent supernovas in the Milky Way, in 1572 and 1604. Neither has produced a bright synchrotron source such as the Crab.

Something is still generating energy inside the Crab Nebula.

In the mid-1960's, astronomers began firing rockets laden with x-ray detectors up above the limits of the Earth's atmosphere. Our planet's air absorbs x-rays, so that we can never detect celestial x-ray sources from the ground. Sure enough, one of the strongest x-ray sources discovered was the good old Crab Nebula! So the synchroton in the sky was putting out even more energy than previously suspected!

The answer to the Crab Nebula's energy source came in 1967.

Pulsars and Neutron Stars

In the summer of 1967, British astronomers Miss Jocelyn Bell and Anthony Hewish discovered strange pulses of radio energy coming from the general direction of the constellation Vulpecula, the Fox. This is a faint and rather shapeless constellation that lies between the bright stars Vega and Altair. All previously-discovered radio sources in the sky emitted their radio energy continuously. This new source "beeped" on and off, one pulse every 1.337 seconds, with the super-clockwork precision of better than a hundred-thousandth of one percent.

The radio pulses were so precise and regular that a few astronomers seriously considered the possibility that they might be deliberate signals from a civilized race. For a few weeks they were called "LGM" signals—for Little Green Men.

While most astronomers are perfectly willing to believe that there are probably many intelligent forms of life in the universe, they still feel better when they can explain a physical phenomenon as a natural event, using the known laws of physics, rather than the unproven assumption of an alien intelligent race, green or otherwise.

Thomas Gold of Cornell University came up with an explanation for the *pulsars,* as the pulsed radio sources were soon named.

Gold drew his explanation from the fact that several theoreticians had earlier predicted the existence of *neutron stars,* massive

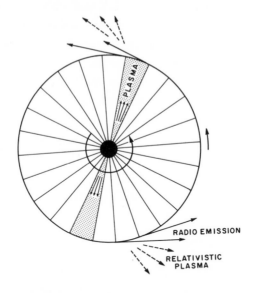

PULSAR MODEL *of* Thomas Gold *pictures the tiny collapsed neutron star spinning rapidly and holding a plasma cloud around it with a strong magnetic field. The plasma is forced to rotate at the same rate that the neutron star does. But at a certain distance, the plasma is spinning at nearly light speed in its effort to keep up with the star's rotation. At this point, some of the plasma breaks free, emitting a sharp pulse of radio and visible radiation.*

stars that had collapsed in on themselves after a supernova explosion. Picture the remains of a star's core, after a supernova explosion. You'd think that such a cataclysm would completely destroy the star, but it doesn't. Not always. For a very massive star, a core can survive, and the core itself might be more massive than the sun.

But this core has now collapsed to an incredibly small size. All its atomic nuclei and electrons have been squeezed together until the electrons are actually forced to merge with the protons of the nuclei, making a star that consists entirely of neutrons (a neutron is a proton and electron combined into one particle).

Such a neutron star, with twice the sun's mass, could be less than 10 kilometers in diameter! The density of a neutron star is in the range of a billion tons per cubic centimeter. A volume the size of your fingertip would weigh a billion tons!

Gold pictured such a neutron star imbedded in a swirling cloud of plasma, as would exist after a supernova explosion. The plasma is permeated by a strong magnetic field. The neutron star, being so fantastically small and dense, must spin at an extraordinarily rapid rate: one complete rotation in a few seconds or less.

Since the plasma is bound to the neutron star by the magnetic field, the star's spin forces the plasma to rotate. The magnetic field in such a case is much stronger than the field in the early sun and its planetary disk; the magnetic field lines would therefore be much "stiffer." The farther away from the star's surface, the faster the plasma must rotate to keep up with the forces pulling it. This is much like a "crack the whip" situation—Tail-End Charlie must go all-out to stay with the rest of the crowd.

At a certain distance out from the neutron star, the plasma just can't keep up, even though it may be racing along at speeds close to the speed of light. The particles that make up the plasma, at this point, break free of the magnetic field and give off a burst of electromagnetic energy. This happens on every rotation of the neutron star, causing a regular periodicity to the pulses.

Gold's theory fitted the conditions in the Crab Nebula extremely well, although no pulsar was known to be there when he first published his ideas. But radio astronomers soon turned their antennas to the Crab once again, and adjusted them to the frequencies that

QUASAR *3C 273 looks like an ordinary bluish star at first glimpse. Yet it is apparently among the most distant objects in the universe, and is giving off more energy than a thousand Milky Way galaxies! (Mt. Wilson and Mt. Palomar Observatories)*

the other pulsars emitted. Sure enough, there was a pulsar sitting in the middle of the Nebula! And this pulsar—this rapidly-spinning neutron star—is the energy source for the Crab's synchrotron radiation. Energetic electrons hurled off by the pulsar's spinning plasma cloud are apparently producing the steady-state radio emissions discovered in the 1940's.

Moreover, Gold's theory predicted that a pulsar should be blinking on and off in visible wavelengths as well as radio. In 1969 the Crab Nebula pulsar was photographed, winking on and off 30 times per second.

Plasma physics had scored an impressive triumph. Hand in hand with nuclear astrophysics, an understanding of plasma processes had allowed scientists to map out the complete lifespan of a star, from its birth in a cloud of dust, to its death throes in the turbulent plasma clouds of a pulsar.

The Violent Universe

The discovery of the pulsars was merely the closing act in a decade such as astronomy has never experienced before. During the 1960's, astronomers found that the placid-looking heavens are anything but serene. Not only do stars explode, whole galaxies erupt in explosions that are thousands of times more powerful than a supernova. And enigmatic objects called *quasars* were discovered; they may be emitting more energy than a thousand galaxies, within a volume of space much smaller than a single galaxy!

The quasars are a special challenge to astronomy, and to plasma physics. They were first discovered by radio telescopes, since they are powerful radio sources. When optical telescopes were trained on the locations of these radio sources, the astronomers saw what appeared to be faint blue stars. They were called "quasi-stellar sources" or "quasi-stellar objects," because they looked like stars but were obviously something more than ordinary stars.

By 1963 it was obvious that the quasars were far outside the Milky Way. They seem to be much smaller than a normal galaxy, but apparently are enormously brighter than any known galaxy. No one knows how far away the quasars are. Some astronomers believe them to be five to ten billion light years distant, the farthest objects man has yet detected. If this is so, then the quasars are beaming out more energy than any normal galaxy.

Other astronomers feel that the quasars are a good deal closer, perhaps "only" a few hundred million light years away. If they are that close, then their energy outputs are not as spectacular as previously believed, although still in a class with full-sized galaxies. The "local" quasar theorists believe that the quasars are objects

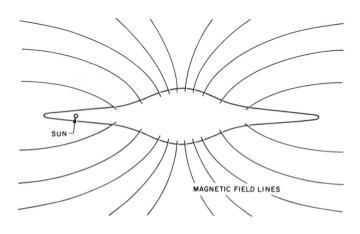

IF THE MILKY WAY EXPLODED, *the shape of the galaxy's magnetic field might steer the violent plasma clouds clear of our solar system. Astronomers suspect that the galaxy did suffer an explosion at its core about a million years ago.*

rather smaller than a galaxy that have been ejected from a parent galaxy, fired off into space like a huge artillery shell.

But where does a galaxy get the energy to blast off an object that's the size of a million or so stars?

By the mid-1960's, astronomers had produced conclusive evidence that galaxies explode. There are violent upheavals going on right now in the heart of several galaxies, and our own Milky Way galaxy may have suffered an explosion at its core as recently as a million years ago. Luckily, we are out toward the fringes of the galaxy and an explosion at the core—some 30,000 light years away

—apparently didn't hurt our solar system. Perhaps the shape of the galactic magnetic field helped to guide the plasma clouds ejected by the explosion into paths that stayed far from our little family of planets.

But again the question arises: where does the energy for a galactic-core explosion come from?

Alfvén, the Swedish physicist who first brought plasma physics into astronomy, has suggested an answer. His answer deals with plasma physics and with *antimatter*.

Antimatter is one of those weird concepts that sounds absolutely impossible until you see the evidence that it actually exists. Antimatter was predicted on theoretical grounds in 1931 by P. A. M. Dirac (born 1902), a British theoretical physicist who won a Nobel Prize in physics in 1933. Dirac postulated that for every type of atomic particle in our universe, there is an antiparticle. For the electron, there's an antielectron that bears a positive charge. For the proton, an antiproton with a negative charge. For the neutron, an antineutron that's still electrically neutral but antimatter all the same. Dirac's theory further showed that when a normal particle meets an antiparticle, they destroy each other completely in a violent flash of energy.

A strange theory. But in 1932 the antielectron was produced in a physics laboratory. It's now called the *positron*. Antiparticles for almost every known subatomic particle have been discovered and identified.

In our corner of the universe, antimatter exists only in laboratories, and only for brief flashes of an instant, deliberately created out of the maelstrom of energy that physicists produce to probe the inner structure of the atom.

The reason antimatter doesn't exist in nature around us is simple: it would be destroyed as soon as it touched normal matter. And it would destroy an equal amount of normal matter in the process. You recall that in the thermonuclear fusion processes that power the sun and stars, 0.7 percent of the hydrogen is converted into energy. When matter and antimatter meet, *all* the material is converted into energy.

If the Moon were made of antimatter, for example, whenever

one of our spacecraft touched it—flash! Both the spacecraft and an equal amount of the antimatter Moon would disappear in a burst of energy.

Many astronomers feel that antimatter does exist in places in the universe. Probably the antimatter stays in its own neighborhood and the normal matter remains in its own territory. For surely whenever they meet they destroy each other.

Alfvén has suggested that antimatter may be powering the quasars and the violent explosions in the cores of galaxies. Indeed, he views the two phenomena as two versions of the same process. Alfvén has pointed out that at the core of a galaxy, the interstellar plasma is at its densest. Throughout the Milky Way galaxy, for example, the density of the interstellar plasma is little more than one atom per cubic centimeter (although it's somewhat higher within our solar system). But at the core of the galaxy, the interstellar plasma clouds are much thicker.

If antimatter exists in the universe, where would it be more likely to show up than in the places where normal matter is thickest? The antimatter should be thickest at the cores of galaxies, too, Alfvén says. And if this is true, then matter-antimatter collisions are inevitable in the cores of galaxies. He suggests that this is exactly what happens in galactic explosions: clouds of matter and antimatter plasmas are colliding and annihilating each other, releasing all the energy available from their total destruction. The quasars, in Alfvén's view, are merely younger, even-more-violent galactic core explosions.

Whether or not the quasars are matter-antimatter explosions, observations have shown that they can be nothing but plasma. And both their visible light and radio output are strongly polarized, leading to the conclusion that they are synchrotron sources, much as the Crab Nebula but on a stupendously larger scale.

The quasars are still a puzzle. But one thing seems clear: only an understanding of plasma physics can unravel the super-energetic processes that power these enigmatic objects.

We've come a long way in our look at the influence of plasma physics on astronomical thinking. We've seen the birth of our solar system and the death of stars and the explosions of whole galaxies.

Now it's time to come back from the edges of the known universe, back to the familiar region of the solar system as it is today, to take a closer look at the world of plasma that exists just a hundred kilometers or so over our heads.

FOUR

Plasmas and the Weather in Space

Until the late 1950's, most scientists pictured the Earth's magnetic field as a simple dipole, like the field of a bar magnet. They drew sketches of the magnetic field extending into space, as simple and regular as the pattern iron filings make around a bar magnet. And they assumed that "outer space" was a virtual vacuum, empty and still.

But they had known for about a century that flares on the sun are often followed by sudden and violent fluctuations in the Earth's magnetic field. This puzzled astronomers and geophysicists alike. How could a magnetic disturbance travel some 150 million kilometers of emptiness?

The answer, of course, is that interplanetary space isn't quite empty. It's a plasma; an extremely low-density plasma, but a plasma nonetheless. Typically, there are only some 10 particles per cubic centimeter between the planets, compared to the 10^{19} or so molecules per cubic centimeter in air at sea level. The density of the interplanetary plasma is so low that a sphere the size of the Earth would contain only eight pounds of material!

Yet this is not a complete void. The plasma between the planets is fully ionized, and there are also tremendous energies in space: electromagnetic radiations, magnetic fields, clouds of high-energy particles, an ethereal wind blowing outward from the sun, and enormously energetic particles born in the sun and even in other stars, thousands of light years distant.

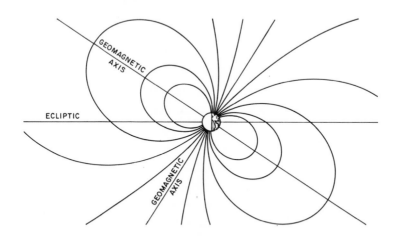

PRE-SPACE AGE VIEW *of the Earth's magnetic field was overly simplified. No one knew then of the Van Allen belts, the solar wind, or the plasma interactions that take place just above our atmosphere.*

There is weather, of a sort, in space. Potentially man-killing weather. The interplanetary plasma may be very rarefied, but it's far from a placid nothingness.

And thanks to satellites and interplanetary probes, we know that our planet Earth, even though it's some 150 million kilometers from the sun, is in a very real sense orbiting inside the sun's far-reaching shell of plasma.

The Magnetic Sun

To understand the weather in space, we must understand the behavior of the sun. For the sun is a titanic, seething display of plasma fireworks, where energies that dwarf everything else in the solar system are commonplace, where magnetic fields and incandescent plasmas are in constant turmoil, and where the weather in space is born. As we'll soon see, man's understanding of the sun and its plasma fireworks is far from complete. But enough is known to answer some questions—and to raise many more.

We must keep in mind two important ideas that deal with plasmas and MHD forces: the ideas of how magnetic fields behave and of plasmas with magnetic fields "frozen" into them.

We've seen that magnetic fields can be thought of as invisible lines of magnetic force, endless loops that can be stretched to almost any size or shape. The strength of a magnetic field, then, is determined by the number of field lines in a given volume. If the field is compressed—as it was when the infant sun contracted from its original dust cloud—then the number of field lines per unit of volume becomes greater and the field intensifies. If something causes the field lines to spread apart, then the field becomes weaker.

It's important to realize, though, that magnetic field lines are purely imaginary. They're a convenient way to visualize the invisible, an invention of the human mind that's helpful, but not real. Magnetic fields exist in the real world, but not field lines.

Magnetic fields can be "frozen in" to a plasma. It's strange to speak of freezing in connection with high-temperature plasmas, but the idea is basically this: Under the conditions in and around the sun, there's a strong coupling between magnetic fields and plasmas. They're locked together, like a rubber band frozen into an ice cube. Where one goes, the other goes also. A force that tends to move the magnetic field will also drag along the plasma attached to it. And any movement of the plasma will bring its "frozen in" magnetic field along, too.

While Hale discovered strong magnetic fields in sunspots and announced discovery of a weaker general magnetic field of the sun, the general field wasn't measured with any real precision until the American father-and-son team of Harold D. Babcock (born 1882) and Horace W. Babcock (born 1912) developed the needed high-precision equipment and techniques. Between measurements of the magnetic fields on the sun and development of plasma and MHD theory, a partial understanding of the sun's behavior has been achieved.

In Chapter 3 we saw that the shining disk of the sun is called the photosphere, and it's actually a layer of plasma without a distinct

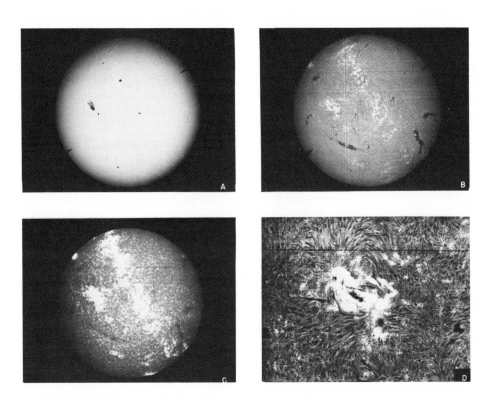

FOUR VIEWS OF THE SUN: *(A) As the sun appears in normal white light. (B) Through a filter that shows the red light of ionized hydrogen; the brightest areas are those richest in hydrogen. (C) In the violet light of ionized calcium. (D) Close-up in hydrogen's light showing the magnetic structure around a sunspot. (Mt. Wilson and Mt. Palomar Observatories)*

surface. Above it is the chromosphere, some 15,000 kilometers thick. And growing out of the chromosphere plasma is the corona. Deep inside the sun is the core where thermonuclear reactions are taking place. The energy from this nuclear furnace literally bubbles out of the photosphere; actual bubbles of plasma a few hundred kilometers across have been photographed. These *convection cells* are heated in the sun's interior, rise to the photosphere, and then in about eight minutes cool enough to sink down again and be replaced by a new convection cell of plasma. Each of these "bubbles" is about the size of Pennsylvania.

Dotting the sun's visible disk are the enigmatic sunspots. They come and go in rather uneven cycles that average about 11 years, although some astronomers believe that this is only half of a true cycle and the full cycle takes some 22–23 years. The sun is seldom completely free of sunspots, but at the height of a cycle, spots large enough to swallow all the planets of the solar system troop across the face of the sun by the dozen.

Sunspots are usually found in pairs or groups. The spot furthest advanced in the direction of the sun's rotation is called the leading spot, the one behind it is the following sunspot. The leading and following sunspots of a pair have opposite magnetic polarity. If the leader is plus, the follower is negative, and *vice-versa*. The standard way of assigning plus and negative values is simple: the place where magnetic lines of force come out of the surface is called plus, or positive polarity; the place where the force lines go back into the surface is minus or negative polarity.

The magnetic fields associated with sunspots range from a few hundred gauss to more than 3500 gauss. There are also extended regions of the photosphere where there are no sunspots, but the magnetic field intensity has risen to 30–50 gauss. These regions change considerably from day to day, whereas sunspots stay relatively stable for many days, even weeks.

Like the sunspots, these extended regions are usually *bipolar*. They have two areas of opposite polarity. The bipolar regions start off as quite compact, well-defined areas where the sun's faint general field suddenly increases markedly from a fraction of a gauss to as much as 50 gauss. Then the region expands while the magnetic field grows even stronger. But soon the field strength levels off, and as the region continues to expand, the field weakens.

When a bipolar region's magnetic field strength is below 20 gauss, there's no visible change in the sun's disk. Above 20 gauss, the area produces *flaculae*, regions that appear bright in the light of ionized calcium atoms. Bipolar regions of even stronger magnetic fields often produce sunspots.

There have been a few observations of *unipolar* magnetic regions on the sun. This is puzzling, because a unipolar region presents a picture of magnetic field lines coming up out of the sun's photosphere and going—where? Significantly, each time a unipolar region has crossed the center of the sun's disk, so that it's facing Earth, there's been a marked increase in cosmic ray activity in the Earth's upper atmosphere, and a few days later, a disturbance in the Earth's magnetic field.

The sun's general magnetic field is often referred to as the *poloidal field,* since it's associated with a north and south magnetic pole that are located near the geographic poles of the sun. But any resemblance between the sun's poloidal field and the Earth's dipole magnetic field stops right there.

The sun's poloidal field reaches an intensity of a few gauss, at times, compared to the Earth's 0.6 gauss field. But at times the sun's field dwindles down to zero, only to reappear—reversed! The north magnetic pole is where the south used to be, and *vice versa.* The reversals of the poloidal field apparently occur at the time of maximum sunspot activity, and are certainly linked to the total magnetic behavior of the sun.

We've assumed that the sun's magnetic field dates back to the magnetic field that was "frozen" into the original dust cloud from which the solar system was created. Even if this isn't so, the sun could generate intense magnetic fields on its own, much the same way an electrical generator produces electric current. In fact, many astrophysicists have suggested that the sun is a sort of "dynamo": a sphere of electrically conducting plasma that is in constant motion (both from spinning on its axis and from internal boiling) will generate strong magnetic fields and electric currents within itself. Geophysicists have also thought that the Earth's magnetic field stems from "dynamo" action in our planet's core of molten, electrically conductive iron.

The sun rotates in an unusual way. The polar regions turn once

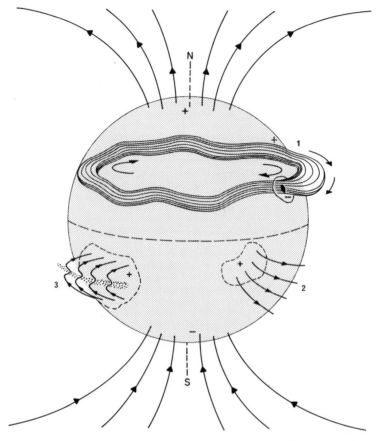

MAGNETIC ACTIVITY ON THE SUN *takes many forms. The general, or poloidal field at the north and south poles is quite weak, but apparently shapes the corona. Under-surface currents, somewhat like terrestrial jetstreams, are thought to cause the observed bipolar magnetic regions (1) which often give rise to sunspots and solar flares. Unipolar regions (2) are unexplained, but may be linked with the production of high-energy cosmic rays. Other bipolar regions (3) support hydrogen clouds called prominences, such as the one shown on p. 34.*

every 34 days, while the equatorial region needs only about 25 days to make a complete rotation. These numbers come from tracking sunspots as they march across the sun's disk, since there's nothing else on the sun to pinpoint. The sun's *differential rotation* is proof that it can't be solid or liquid. But it's also a strong hint that there must be turbulent currents within the sun, possibly just under the visible disk, where the regions that rotate at different rates "rub" against each other.

Here on Earth we have a somewhat similar phenomenon in our atmosphere. Global air patterns produce *jet streams*, strong rivers of fast-flowing air that mark the boundary between two dissimilar parts of the atmosphere. Earthly jet streams are gaseous, of course. On the sun, there might be plasma jet streams, with all the MHD forces associated with moving electrical charges.

Many astrophysicists have pictured the sun's jet streams as producing *toroidal magnetic fields*, that is, ring-shaped magnetic fields that arch around the sun in the regions where the fast-moving equatorial plasma meets the slower-moving polar plasmas. There's a toroidal field in both the northern and southern hemispheres, at about 50° or 60° latitude, running roughly parallel to the sun's equator.

The toroidal fields must have very interesting interactions with the convection currents of hot plasma welling up from the sun's interior. But not much is known, even in theory, about this. Apparently, the toroidal field is often forced up to the surface and even slightly out of it, into the chromosphere, by these rising convection currents. Once the field breaks through to the surface, it produces many of the magnetic effects observed from Earth.

The bipolar regions can be pictured as areas where the toroidal field has broken out of the surface and looped back into the photosphere again. Sunspots are bipolar regions where the magnetic fields are more intense. The sunspots appear dark because they're cooler than the surrounding photosphere plasma, but Galileo showed about 350 years ago that the sunspots are actually very hot and bright—they appear dark only by contrast to the gleaming photosphere. It seems that MHD forces stemming from the toroidal field are somehow cooling off the plasma in a sunspot. But just how this works no one knows. Yet.

Often a cloud of glowing plasma will be seen hanging thousands of kilometers above the photosphere. Sometimes it's arched up from the surface. At other times, it seems to form out of nothingness and hover above the photosphere until it slowly dissolves (uncannily like rainclouds in our atmosphere). These *prominences,* as they're called, are most likely supported by loops of the toroidal field.

In the areas of the sun that show strong magnetic fields—the bipolar regions, sunspots, unipolar regions, and the areas around the poles where the poloidal field can be detected—radio telescopes have found radio wavelength emissions. This is to be expected, because the magnetic fields are doubtlessly accelerating electrons and protons through the chromosphere in these regions, and such processes would lead to the generation of radio noise.

The most intense bursts of radio energy, however, come from the solar flares. We'll discuss them in more detail later in this chapter.

The Corona and Plasma Waves

The chromosphere and corona have presented astronomers with a puzzle that only plasma physics can solve.

The chromosphere is a tenuous layer of plasma. When seen during an eclipse or in a coronagraph (a special telescope fitted with a filter that blots out the main disk of the sun), the chromosphere shows up as a flickering red band of plasma, once described as looking like "a burning prairie."

In the 1950's, astronomers began to realize that something very strange happens in the chromosphere. The temperature of the photosphere is some 6000°K. But the temperature in the corona was found to be about 1,000,000°K. In the chromosphere, plasma temperature is rising steeply. But simple thermodynamics shows that just the opposite should be happening!

One of the basic tenets of physics is that heat always flows from a hot region to a cooler one. Heat is generated deep inside the sun's interior and radiates away from the surface of the photosphere. If the corona is hotter than the photosphere, then the heat should flow in the opposite direction, down toward the sun's surface. If *that* happened, we wouldn't be getting any heat from the sun.

Obviously, the sun's heat is flowing outward from the corona and radiating away into space.

Then how can the corona have a higher temperature than the photosphere?

The answer is that a high temperature doesn't always mean more heat. The corona has a very low density, only about 10^{-11} the density of the air we breathe. There's very little actual material in the corona. Individual particles can be accelerated in such a thin plasma to very high velocities, and we measure these velocities as temperature. Temperature can be thought of as a measure of the energy invested in an average particle in a plasma. Heat is the total amount of energy in all the particles.

Since the corona is low in density, it can have a very high temperature (energetic particles) without much heat (low number of particles). You could freeze to death in such a high-temperature plasma!

The principles of thermodynamics are not in danger. But an important question remains. How does the corona get such a high temperature? There's something pumping energy into the corona particles, something other than simple heat radiation.

Alfvén provided the answer. He pointed out that in a plasma, energy can be transferred by the magnetic field, through MHD interactions. It seems clear that the chromosphere is heavily laced with magnetic fields, both from the arches of the toroidal fields that cause sunspots and prominences, and from the general poloidal field. The poloidal field, although much weaker than any other, must extend very far out into the corona. Eclipse pictures have shown the corona's magnetically-shaped streamers.

The turbulent energy of violently agitated plasma in the photosphere makes these magnetic field lines vibrate, somewhat in the manner that a harpist's fingers can make the strings of his instrument vibrate. In a plasma, the electrons and ions tend to lock themselves onto magnetic field lines. They spiral around a field line, linked to it by electromagnetic force. While they can slide up and down a field line quite easily, like a ring on a piece of rope, it's very difficult for the particles to move from one field line to another, to jump across field lines. This "tethering" effect is called the *Lorentz*

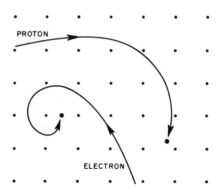

LORENTZ FORCE *influences motion of charged particles in a magnetic field. Positively-charged protons are turned in one direction, negative electrons oppositely. The proton's turning radius is much larger because it is a heavier particle and more difficult to turn.*

force, after the Dutch physicist Hendrick A. Lorentz (1853–1928). Thus, in a plasma permeated by a magnetic field, the particles tend to spiral along in the direction of the field, and can cut across the field only with great difficulty.

When the magnetic field vibrates, the electrons and ions linked to the field are forced to move also. Energy can be transferred this way, and Alfvén suggested that this is how energy is imparted to the corona.

The corona's high temperature, then, is due to MHD forces that Alfvén called *hydromagnetic waves*. This mechanism of transferring energy from a magnetic field to the particles of a plasma is also referred to as *plasma waves*, although most physicists call the phenomenon—quite justly—*Alfvén waves*.

The Solar Wind

While astronomers and physicists were puzzling over the high temperature of the corona, rocket engineers were building the first satellites and rocket probes. The instruments in the early *Luniks*,

Mariners and *Explorers* showed what Earth-based scientists had begun to suspect: that there's a stream of ionized hydrogen wafting out from the sun.

This *solar wind,* as it's now called, ordinarily passes the Earth at about 400 kilometers per second. But during the violent sequence of events that follows a solar flare, the solar wind can become an interplanetary hurricane of more than 1500 kilometers per second.

Please realize that, despite its name and high velocity, the solar wind is invisible, impalpable, and undetectable to any but the most sensitive instruments. In the deep vacuum of space, though, the solar wind plays an important role in carrying energy and matter from the sun. In some ways, it has the same relationship to the weather in space as the prevailing winds of our atmosphere have on terrestrial weather.

Although the solar wind was discovered in the late 1950's, the Norwegian physicist Olaf K. Birkeland (1867–1917) suggested in 1896 that the brilliant aurorae—the Northern and Southern Lights —might be caused by a stream of ionized particles coming from the sun. And furthermore, there's been a clue to the existence of the solar wind that's as old as mankind himself, and far older.

Comets appear in our skies quite frequently, often bright enough to see with the naked eye. In ancient times they caused terror and were thought to be harbingers of disaster. Today astronomers sometimes refer to them as "solar windsocks." For, just as a windsock at an airport indicates which way the wind is blowing, a comet's tail always points away from the sun, showing which way the solar wind is blowing.

If you think for a moment about the sun's corona, you might come to the conclusion that there must be a solar wind. For a cloud of plasma, even a tenuous plasma such as the corona, normally doesn't hang suspended in space. Why doesn't the corona collapse back into the sun? Surely the sun's gravitational attraction is pulling it in that direction.

The reason lies in the corona's very high temperature. While there's not much heat in this million-degree plasma, the individual particles are still moving at enormous velocities. Their energy of motion forces the corona to expand, rather than collapse. And the farther away from the sun, the faster this expansion must be.

The pearly-white corona that's seen during eclipses is only part of the sun's true corona. This visible corona is the part that's close enough to the sun, and dense enough, to reflect the light coming up from the photosphere. But the corona goes on far beyond the visible halo around the sun, expanding more and more rapidly and turning into the solar wind that our spacecraft have detected. Our planet, then, orbits within the streaming plasma of the sun's corona.

Eclipse photos have shown that the sun's magnetic field affects the inner, visible corona. Theory tells us that the solar wind should carry along part of this magnetic field with it. And as the corona expands, the field should weaken. In the Earth's neighborhood, this field is calculated to be down to between 2 and 4×10^{-5} gauss. Space probes have measured the magnetic field in interplanetary space and found values within this range. But as we'll soon see, there's a complicated interplay between the solar wind and the Earth's magnetic field.

Incidentally, for very small magnetic field values, physicists use a unit called the *gamma*. One gamma is equal to 10^{-5} gauss.

Spacecraft have proved the existence of the solar wind and measured its magnetic field. There's still some argument among astrophysicists as to whether this field should be considered part of the sun's magnetic field or thought of as part of the field that pervades the entire Milky Way galaxy. Generally, it's referred to as the interplanetary magnetic field, leaving aside the argument about its origin.

If the sun didn't rotate at all, the solar wind would flow out smoothly in all directions through the solar system. And the magnetic field frozen into the solar wind's plasma would stream out with it, like the spokes of a wheel. But the sun does rotate, and not all at the same rate, either. And there are flares and prominences on the sun, and unipolar regions, all of which hurl plasma clouds of particles and magnetic field energy out into interplanetary space.

The result is that the solar wind is gusty. The interplanetary magnetic field is twisted, looped, kinked. And when this flow of plasma reaches the Earth, a very interesting and complex situation arises.

The Earth's Magnetic Umbrella

Man didn't discover the solar wind until rockets carried detection instruments into space. This is because we're sheltered from the solar wind by a vast, strong magnetic shield. The Earth's magnetic field provides us with an umbrella against the weather in space.

There are two regions where the umbrella leaks: at the magnetic

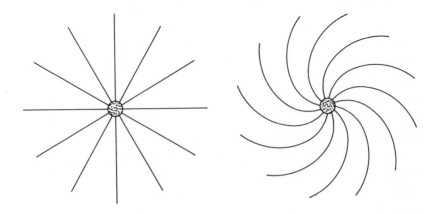

SUN'S MAGNETIC FIELD *shapes the flow of the solar wind. If the sun did not rotate, solar wind would flow out evenly in all directions (left). But sun's rotation causes magnetic field lines to spiral, complicating solar wind flow. Actually, solar flares and other disturbances make the field lines "kinky" and cause unpredictable changes in the intensity of the solar wind.*

poles. In these Arctic and Antarctic regions the Earth's magnetic field bends down and connects with the atmosphere and surface. Here the gleaming aurorae often bring eerie light to the dark sky. The Northern and Southern Lights look very much like the beautiful plasma glows produced in discharge tubes. And for good reason.

We've seen that the Earth's magnetic field, called the *geomagnetic field*, is about 0.6 gauss. It may originate from "dynamo" action in the planet's core of molten iron, where electromagnetic currents can be created by the motion of the Earth's rotation.

Until the Space Age, geophysicists generally pictured the Earth's field as a simple dipole, as if a bar magnet were stuck through our planet. But as early as 1907, the Norwegian physicist Carl Stormer (1874–1957) showed mathematically that there could be much more going on not far above our heads. He calculated that there could be a belt of ionized particles trapped in the geomagnetic field, slightly above the outer fringes of our atmosphere. Stormer was following his countryman Birkeland's earlier idea that particles coming from the sun caused the aurorae.

For the most part, few scientists paid attention to the possible interactions between the geomagnetic field and solar activity, except for the puzzling fluctuations of the geomagnetic field. These *magnetic storms* played havoc with long-distance radio communications. It seemed obvious that magnetic storms violently disrupted the ionosphere and radically changed the layers of radio-reflecting ionized gases high in the Earth's atmosphere. The aurorae also flamed brilliantly during magnetic storms.

The first artificial satellite launched successfully by the United States, *Explorer I* (31 January 1958), carried a Geiger counter to measure radiation levels in space. It was known that *cosmic rays* were bombarding the Earth's upper atmosphere. The Geiger counter was to measure the intensity of this radiation.

Surprisingly, the counter showed very little radiation in space. When the satellite crossed the Earth's equatorial region, the Geiger counter usually went silent altogether. Another Geiger counter aboard Explorer III performed the same way.

How could there be cosmic rays striking the Earth's atmosphere, but none in orbit just a few hundred kilometers above the ground? James A. Van Allen (born 1914) of the State University of Iowa, was especially puzzled, since he was responsible for the radiation-measuring experiments aboard the satellites. Perhaps, he and others thought, the counters aren't registering a low radiation level at all. Perhaps the radiation level is much higher than anyone expected, so high that the counters are saturated. The situation might be something like a small boy who's crammed so much food into his mouth that he can't tell you how much he's enjoying the meal.

Later satellites carried more sophisticated radiation measuring instruments, capable of recording much higher radiation fluxes. And they showed that, indeed, there were two vast belts of very high radiation levels girdling the Earth. They were immediately named the *Van Allen radiation belts*.

Radiation in the lower Van Allen belt comes mainly from high-

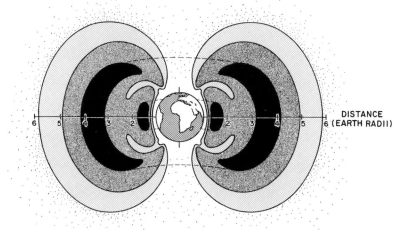

THE VAN ALLEN BELTS *as they would appear if there were no solar wind. Darkest regions are areas of strongest radiation levels. Note that regions between belts are not empty.*

energy protons. The lower belt is centered some 3000 kilometers above the Earth's magnetic equator. About 15,000 kilometers out the upper belt contains very energetic electrons. Both belts curve around and dip toward the atmosphere near the geomagnetic poles.

As you might suspect, the belts reach the upper atmosphere in the regions where the aurorae shine.

Although the belts are vast enough to circle the globe, there's very little matter in them. All the material in both Van Allen belts amounts to less mass than a single astronaut!

But the particles in the belts are very energetic. Physicists often use a unit called the *electron volt* to represent the energy of an atomic particle. The electron volt is a very tiny unit of energy, equivalent to about 10^{-12} erg. But protons with energies of 20 to 40

million electron volts (MeV) can easily penetrate a centimeter or
more of lead. The protons in the lower Van Allen belt are about this
energetic, and some of them get up to energies like 600 MeV. The
only radiation detected in space that's more energetic are the
cosmic rays, some of the particles fired off from the sun in solar
flares, and the particles accelerated in laboratories by man-made
machines such as synchrotrons.

The outer Van Allen belt's radiation comes mainly from electrons, and there seem to be two different types of activity among
them. There's a fairly steady level of rather low-energy electrons,
at a few tens of thousands of electron volts (20–40 keV). But there's
also a fluctuating number of higher-energy electrons, with peak
energies in the low MeV range. These high-energy peaks seem to
be related to geomagnetic storms.

Thousands or even millions of electron volts may not sound like
much energy. But several satellites that orbited with the Van Allen
belts have had their electronic gear disrupted or even disabled by
the radiation there. If an astronaut spent much time in the belts
without some form of radiation shielding, he would be killed.

Once the belts were found, the next question was: How did they
get there? Apparently, the incoming cosmic-ray particles (cosmic
rays are not rays, but particles), are responsible for the inner belt.
Cosmic-ray particles are mostly protons. Most of these high-energy
protons bore right through the geomagnetic field and strike the
atmosphere. But there are some that come in at such an angle and
at low enough energy that the geomagnetic field can trap them and
store them in the lower belt.

We've seen earlier that a charged particle moving in a magnetic
field tends to spiral around a magnetic field line, due to the Lorentz
force. On the outer Van Allen belt, a 100 MeV proton would make
a spiral that's nearly 5000 kilometers in diameter. A 100 keV proton's loop would be less than 200 kilometers' diameter, and a 100
keV electron—because of its smaller mass and momentum—would
make a loop less than two kilometers across.

The geomagnetic field is concentrated at the poles and spread at
its widest around the equator. A particle that comes in from space
is trapped by the field and goes spiralling along a field line. As the

field lines grow more and more concentrated toward the poles, the particle's spiral is forced into a tighter, smaller loop, until finally it "mirrors" and actually begins moving in the opposite direction. A particle heading toward the north magnetic pole will "mirror" and begin heading for the south pole. A round trip from the northern to the southern hemisphere takes only a few seconds.

The particles also drift across the Earth in longitude. Electrons drift eastward, protons westward. It takes from a few minutes to a few hours for a particle to circle the world this way.

While the Van Allen belt particles are racing back and forth from pole to pole, "mirroring" to reverse course, and drifting around the planet, many of them inevitably are dumped out of the belt and into the atmosphere. This usually happens around the poles. A

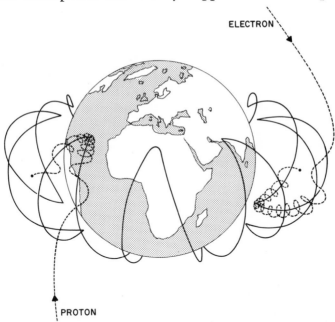

VAN ALLEN PARTICLES "MIRROR" *as they travel along geomagnetic field lines. Electrons and protons spiral around field lines, but as the field lines draw close together near the poles, the particles "mirror" and reverse direction. Electrons drift eastward, protons westward. They can circle the world in no more than a few hours, sometimes in a few minutes.*

particle will get low enough to run into significant atmospheric density. All through its travels in space, the particle has suffered few collisions, if any. At a density of 10 particles per cubic centimeter, the mean free path of a particle is more than 100 million kilometers! There are very few collisions in the interplanetary plasma, and in fact it's often referred to as a *collisionless plasma.*

But if a particle bites deep enough into the atmosphere, it will undergo many collisions. It will quickly recombine with atmospheric electrons or protons to form a neutral atom. Thus the Van Allen belt loses particles.

The belts don't waste away and disappear, though, because new particles are arriving to replenish them. We've seen that cosmic-ray protons probably feed the lower belt. Electrons from the solar wind and other outbursts on the sun probably populate the outer belt.

It's important to realize that although we've spoken of the belts as containing either protons or electrons, they in fact contain both together. The highest-energy particles in the inner belt are protons; and the most energetic particles in the outer belt, electrons. But in both belts, and in the regions around and in between the belts, there are *both* protons and electrons. The Earth is surrounded by a neutral, fully-ionized plasma.

The Magnetosphere

Ten years of satellite measurements and laboratory work have shown how this plasma surrounding the Earth—which is now called the *magnetosphere*—interacts with the solar wind.

The Earth creates a shock wave in the solar wind, somewhat like the bow wave made by a boat as it cuts through water. But the shock wave in the solar wind isn't made by the solid body of our planet, it's made by the magnetosphere. It's a magnetohydrodynamic shock wave.

Shock waves produced on Earth, such as a sonic boom, are caused by molecules colliding with each other. Typically, the shock wave is no thicker than a few mean free paths of the molecules. But the particles in the magnetosphere have mean free paths in excess of 100 million kilometers, and the shock wave there is only 100 kilometers thick. Clearly, particle collisions can't cause the MHD shock wave.

Collisionless plasmas have been investigated in several laboratories, and even before the discovery of the shock wave in space, plasma physicists were predicting that the Earth's magnetosphere would cause a collisionless, MHD shock on the sunward side of our planet.

If the particles aren't colliding, how does energy get transferred in a collisionless shock wave? In an ordinary shock wave, particle collisions transfer the energy, like billiard balls hitting each other. Without some mechanism of energy transfer a shock wave can't be sustained.

The energy transfer is apparently accomplished by the plasma's magnetic field. The solar wind consists not merely of particles, but a magnetic field as well. This field, with a strength of some 20 to 40 gammas near the Earth, is rippled constantly by Alfvén waves generated on the sun. As the field lines undulate, they drag along the particles attached to them.

When the solar wind meets the Earth's magnetosphere, both the geomagnetic field and the interplanetary field are compressed, squeezed against each other. Satellite measurements have shown that the field intensity fluctuates sharply in the shock front. It is this "battling" of magnetic field energies that sustains the shock wave. In the process, some of the solar-wind particles apparently are dislodged from the interplanetary field and are attached to the geomagnetic field. This is most likely a prime source of particles for the outer Van Allen belt.

Behind this shock front, the magnetosphere has the shape of a vast teardrop, much like the streamlines found around a sphere in a wind tunnel. On the sunward side of the magnetosphere the solar wind flattens the geomagnetic field considerably, pushing it closer to the planet's surface than it would be if there were no wind. On the night side, the magnetosphere is blown back into a long tail, so elongated that no spacecraft has yet found its full extent. Probably the magnetosphere tail goes beyond the orbit of the Moon, some 400,00 kilometers away.

When there's little activity on the sun, the "upwind" side of the magnetosphere extends out to about 10 Earth radii (1 Earth radius = 6371 km), with the shock wave standing out slightly

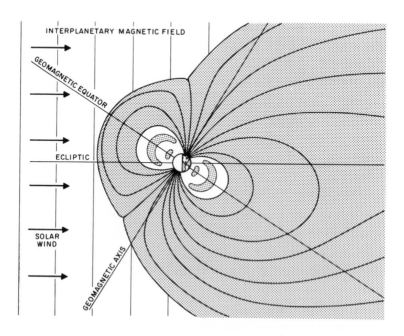

EARTH'S MAGNETOSPHERE *is caused by interactions of the solar wind, geomagnetic field, and trapped particles such as those in the Van Allen regions. Sunward side of the magnetosphere is pressed in toward Earth by the solar wind, while the magnetosphere's "tail" presumably extends past the orbit of the Moon.*

ahead of the main body of the magnetosphere, about 14 radii. But during a strong solar disturbance, the magnetosphere can be pushed back to eight Earth radii, flattened by the increased pressure of the solar wind.

Cosmic Rays

There's another factor involved in the weather in space, a factor we've touched on a few times already: cosmic rays.

They're called rays, but actually they're particles. They were named before their nature was understood, back in the nineteenth century when it became apparent that some form of radiation akin to radioactivity was coming from space. Today we know that the cosmic "rays" are really atomic nuclei, stripped of their electrons and accelerated to enormous energies. About 85% of the cosmic particles are hydrogen nuclei, bare protons. Some 14% are helium nuclei, and the remaining one percent consists of the heavier elements.

Cosmic particles are the most energetic bits of matter discovered by man, with energies that range beyond 10^{20} electron volts—a hundred billion billion eV. In contrast, the best that physicists have been able to produce in their giant "atom smashing" particle accelerators is to impart some 30 billion electron volts (30 BeV) to particles such as electrons and protons.

Most cosmic particles strike the Earth's atmosphere with less spectacular (but still awesome) energies of 500 MeV to a few BeV. The least energetic cosmic particles are never detected on Earth; the geomagnetic field traps them and they help to populate the Van Allen belts.

But cosmic particles of about 500 MeV or greater are energetic enough to penetrate the geomagnetic umbrella and hit our atmosphere. Here they quickly collide with molecules in the air and set off cascades of secondary particles, like a bowling ball knocking pins in all directions. The cosmic radiation detected on the ground is almost entirely this secondary radiation, which is often energetic enough to be detected in mines deep underground.

Every minute of your life, several of these secondary particles—shattered molecular shrapnel—strike your body. While they cause no obvious, direct biological effects, cosmic particles may have a very long-range impact on Earthly life. Many biologists believe that cosmic radiation has caused genetic mutations and thereby has played a significant role in the evolution of life on Earth.

In space, without our thick blanket of air to protect them, astronauts are exposed to primary cosmic particles, not merely the secondaries we get on the ground. Several astronauts have reported seeing tiny flashes of light in their spacecraft cabins that might have been cosmic particles hitting air molecules with enough energy to cause visible light. But even though they're extremely energetic, cosmic particles aren't enough to pose a serious radiation hazard in space. There's normally only one such particle per cubic meter at a given instant of time. And the metal of the spacecraft's skin and equipment stops all but the highest-energy particles, which are (thankfully) the rarest type of all.

As we'll see in a moment, there's a much more serious radiation hazard in space due to solar flares.

Solar flares produce cosmic radiation. Shortly after a flare is seen on the sun, cosmic particles with energies of 10 BeV and more have been detected in the upper atmosphere. But most of the steady drizzle of cosmic radiation, including the most energetic particles, comes from far beyond the solar system. Apparently the remains of old supernovas, such as the Crab Nebula, are a source of cosmic particles. In their wildly-distorted plasma clouds and magnetic fields, these cosmic synchrotrons accelerate particles to fantastic energies and spew them out into insterstellar space. Perhaps the magnetic field of the galaxy plays a role in guiding or even further accelerating the particles. And with the recent discoveries of quasars and exploding galaxies, astrophysicists are now wondering if these titanic forces, which dwarf individual supernovas, might not be still another source of cosmic-radiation particles.

Solar Flares and Magnetic Storms

The most violent event in the solar system is a flare on the sun. A typical solar flare will release about 10^{33} ergs, which is equal to ten million *billion* tons of TNT exploding (10^{10} megatons). Since the whole sun emits 3.8×10^{33} ergs per second, a flare represents something like a quarter-second's worth of the sun's total energy output.

Strangely, most flares are rather inconspicuous when viewed in visible light. But they produce an intense burst of radio noise, together with strong ultraviolet and x-ray "light." And when a flare is positioned on the sun so that it can influence the Earth, for several days afterward we feel its effects. The magnetosphere buckles and rings like a cymbal; radiation levels in the Van Allen belts fluctuate wildly; the aurorae flame with fierce beauty, sometimes as far south as Florida; the influx of cosmic rays is disturbed; radio communication can be disrupted for days; and any astronaut in an unshielded spacecraft outside the magnetosphere would die in a matter of hours, if not minutes.

Flares usually come from active sunspot regions. Often they erupt with no warning, and not much visible light. On other occasions, there's first a build-up of a glowing prominence, a seething cloud of plasma the size of a continent, that hangs above the sunspots region for a half-hour or so. Generally there's a weak emission of x-ray and radio energy coming from the prominence as it hangs in the chromosphere. This radiation probably comes from electrons that are being accelerated and excited by the magnetic fields that hold the prominence in place.

Then the flare bursts out, with an intense flash of radio, ultraviolet and x-ray emission. The plasma of the prominence is hurled away from the sun at some 1500 kilometers per second. A surface wave surges across the photosphere, spreading outward at about 1000 km/sec, looking like a wave made in the ocean by an underwater explosion.

Apparently the magnetic field around the sunspot, which was holding the prominence, somehow collapses and dumps its energy into accelerating the plasma cloud.

The electromagnetic radiation from the flare—visible light, radio, UV and x-rays—reaches Earth in 8.3 minutes. It's the harbinger of more serious things to come. Following the electromagnetic energy by a few minutes or a few hours is the first wave of extremely energetic protons and electrons. These particles travel through the interplanetary plasma as though it didn't exist, hurtling along at speeds that become "relativistic"—close to the speed of light. Their actual transit time between the sun and Earth depends both on the intensity of the flare and the alignment of the interplanetary magnetic field.

Being charged particles, they must follow magnetic field lines. If the flare is in a position on the sun where there's no magnetic field "path" to the Earth, we never receive the particles. And even when there is a path linking our planet with the flare, the interplanetary magnetic field is kinked and twisted so much that it may take hours for the particles to reach Earth, rather than minutes.

When these particles do arrive at the Earth, they often burst right through the magnetosphere, they're so energetic. Usually they're detected near the magnetic poles, where the geomagnetic field funnels them into the atmosphere. Sometimes protons from a flare are so powerful—more than 15,000 BeV—that they reach the ground at the equator.

These relativistic particles are the deadliest hazard known to exist in space. The particle flux from a major flare could kill an un-shielded astronaut just as surely as radioactive fallout from an H-bomb—and probably much faster. Men in spacecraft that orbit the Earth inside the protective shell of the magnetosphere are safe from most of this radiation. But for astronauts venturing away from our planet toward the Moon or farther, either some form of shield-ing or a means of predicting the solar "weather" is necessary, as we'll see in Chapter 6.

The incoming hail of particles from a solar flare rises to a maxi-mum in a few hours, or sometimes in a few days. In either event, it continues to bombard the Earth for several days after a flare, taper-ing off in intensity slowly. The total amount of particles ejected by a flare is unknown. The largest flare ever measured, in November 1960, showered such a huge flux of particles on Earth that proton-counting sensors aboard balloons, rockets and satellites couldn't handle the avalanche; most of the detectors were swamped, just as the Geiger counters that originally tried to detect the Van Allen belts were saturated by a radiation level too high for them to record.

When a strong flare makes itself felt on Earth, radio telescopes are usually put out of business for several days. Although such telescopes can study the heavens in bright sunshine and even in rainstorms, the radiation from a solar flare interferes so much with radio emissions coming from beyond the solar system that the radio telescopes are often useless. It takes several days for the electro-magnetic environment around the Earth to clear up enough to allow the radio astronomers to go back to measuring the faint whisperings of the universe.

But the most violent effects of the flare are yet to come.

The flare has ejected a great puff of plasma that travels across interplanetary space, expanding somewhat as it goes, carrying its own magnetic field frozen into it. When this plasma cloud hits the Earth's magnetosphere, we get a magnetic storm that rattles the geomagnetic field, turns on the aurorae to their brightest glow, and drives radio engineers into fits of helpless rage.

Since the middle of the last century it's been known that flares on the sun are often followed by magnetic storms on Earth. And since Marconi's time, radio engineers have known that magnetic storms means unpredictable disruptions in the ionosphere. The reflecting layers of plasma high in the atmosphere go wild, and radio communications are at the mercy of the ionosphere's whim.

Some of these magnetic storms begin very sharply, almost without any warning whatever. Within 12 to 14 hours after a flare on the sun, the Earth's magnetic field suddenly buckles as if it's been hit by a cosmic hammer.

It has been. In 1931 the British geophysicists Sydney Chapman (1888–1970) and V. C. A. Ferraro (born 1907) suggested that a plasma cloud ejected by the sun could cause the sharp compression of the geomagnetic field that's responsible for these "sudden commencement" magnetic storms. In the 1950's Alfvén and other plasma physicists showed that collisionless shock waves could exist in the interplanetary plasma, and such a shock wave would be set off by the impact of a flare's plasma cloud against the magnetosphere. When the plasma cloud hits the magnetosphere, the geomagnetic field acts very much like a drumhead that's hit first by a single, very sharp blow of the drumstick, and then ruffled for some time by continued blows.

The geomagnetic field is compressed drastically: on the sunward side it can get flattened down to half its normal size. The Van Allen belts are violently disturbed; sometimes they dump almost all their particles into the atmosphere and then fill up again within a day or so.

Even the steady infall of cosmic particles is disturbed at this point. The cloud of plasma that compresses the geomagnetic field also shunts aside or absorbs most of the cosmic particles striking

Earthward. This phenomenon, which can last for a day or so, is known as the *Forbush decrease,* after the American physicist Scott E. Forbush (born 1904) who first noticed that cosmic-ray intensity often falls abruptly during a magnetic storm.

Both the geomagnetic field's rattling and the Van Allen belt's dumping of its particles turns the ionosphere into a shambles. The aurorae gleam in their ghostly beauty at latitudes far from their usual haunts, thanks to the huge number of particles being funnelled into the atmosphere. This effect of solar flares must have frightened the wits out of our superstitious ancestors.

Contemporary radio engineers are only slightly less perturbed. High-frequency (HF) and very-high-frequency (VHF) radio communications are often blanked out completely during this phase of a magnetic storm. The ionosphere consist of several layers of plasma, each of which reflects different radio frequencies. During a storm, some layers are intensified so much that they absorb the radio waves instead of reflecting them. Other layers seem to disappear altogether, and the radio frequencies usually reflected by those layers pass straight out into space.

These frustrating tricks of the ionosphere are generally called *polar cap absorption* events (PCA's) by geophysicists. While the radio engineers can often switch to alternate frequencies and, more recently, use satellite relays at frequencies that don't depend on the ionosphere, still most of the world's long-range radio traffic relies on ionospheric reflections, and a magnetic storm plays havoc with communications.

During particularly violent magnetic storms, even telephone cables resting at the bottom of the ocean have been affected by induced magnetic forces and electrical currents that have scrambled signals running through them.

The "emptiness" between sun and Earth, then, is actually a rich domain of plasmas and electromagnetic energies. While the weather in space can cause problems on Earth and is dangerous to astronauts, we'll see in Chapter 6 that plasma technology offers some answers and some protection from the dangers of interplanetary storms.

FIVE

Plasmas for Power

The world faces a critical dilemma.

Modern civilization depends on energy. You have at your fingertips more energy than a Roman emperor could command from a thousand slaves: energy from electricity, for the most part. This energy is more than a convenience, it's a way of life. Anyone who's lived through a power blackout knows how modern civilization depends totally on electrical energy.

In every industrialized nation of the world, the demand for electrical power is increasing steeply, doubling every ten years or even sooner. In the newly developing nations, electrical power is often the first objective of the drive toward industrialization. For without electricity, there can be no factories, no swift communications, no industry, no modernization, no improvement in the economy or the living standards of the people.

Yet despite this enormous demand for more electrical power, it seems clear that we cannot continue to build more and more electrical power-generation plants.

One problem is pollution. Power-generation plants produce air and water pollution. In many parts of the United States, the pollution load is already far more than it should be. Pollution is threatening to alter the very basic ecology of our planet. If unchecked, pollution will ultimately make this world unlivable.

Another problem is simply that you can't keep building power stations indefinitely. If the demand for electrical power continues to grow, we can picture a world covered with power stations, using all the coal, oil, natural gas, uranium, thorium and any other kind of fuel that exists on our planet. And the demand is rising faster than new power plants can be built. There have already been serious blackouts over large parts of the United States. Even more common are "brownouts," where electricity is rationed so that everybody may have enough to live on, while nobody gets as much as he wants.

These problems are, at heart, problems of efficiency. The pollution that power stations produce is a function of their efficiency: the more efficient the power-generation process, the less pollution there will be for every kilowatt of electrical power. And the more efficient power stations become, the fewer stations will be needed. High efficiency stations will be better able to keep up with the growing demand for power than stations of lower efficiency.

There are tremendous energies locked in plasmas. Can these energies be tapped to provide abundant, pollution-free, efficient power?

Ever since Bethe announced that the sun is a thermonuclear reactor, men have dreamed of producing controlled thermonuclear reactors here on Earth. Such fusion reactors could supply a virtually limitless amount of cheap, clean power. In Chapter 7, we'll see that many of the world's best scientists are working hard toward fusion reactors. But the task is formidable, and results may not be forthcoming in this century.

What do we do in the meantime?

Plasma dynamics offers another opportunity: the magnetohydrodynamic generator. Tapping the power of a stream of plasma, MHD generators have been built for experimental purposes. They work now. And when fully developed, they promise to produce electricity with much higher efficiency and much less pollution than conventional power stations can offer.

From Faraday to MHD

Michael Faraday discovered the basic principles of electrical power generation about a century and a half ago. He showed that when a material that conducts electricity is set in motion through a magnetic field, an electric current is generated.

Thomas Edison (1847–1931) turned Faraday's laboratory work into practical reality. In 1882 he showed the world that electricity could be generated reliably and in sufficient quantity to light up a city. Within a few decades most industrial machinery, lighting systems, communications, home appliances, and now even heating and air-conditioning units have been based on the availability of inexpensive, abundant electrical power.

Edison's generators (or dynamos, as they were called) didn't use plasmas. Even if Edison had known about MHD he couldn't have built an MHD generator. There was no way to produce the amount of high-temperature plasma that an MHD generator requires. And no materials that could hold the plasma without being destroyed.

The heart of Edison's dynamo was a bundle of copper wires, called the *armature*. The armature was spun rapidly in a magnetic field. Being a conductor of electricity in motion relative to a magnetic field, the armature had an electric current induced in it. Other coils of copper, called *brushes*, tapped the current and fed it to the outside world.

During the first decade or so after Edison's initial success, there was a battle between those who wanted to build electrical power systems that produced direct current (DC) and those who thought alternating current (AC) was preferable. For reasons we needn't go into here, the AC proponents won. The power you buy today comes in a form where the electrons that make up the current alternate their flow direction sixty times per second (60 cycle AC).

Modern generators, after nearly a century of development, are still based on Edison's design. The heart of the modern generator is still a spinning copper-wire armature, whether the generator was built at the turn of the century or is a brand-new nuclear power plant. And despite intensive engineering efforts, powerplants based on such generators seem limited to efficiencies of about 40%, at best.

A source of mechanical energy is needed to make the armature turn. Modern generators use turbines to provide the mechanical energy. In most systems, steam is used to turn the turbine. Hydroelectric dams use falling water to spin the turbines. And, more recently, generators using gas turbine engines (similar to aircraft jet engines) have come into use for special purposes.

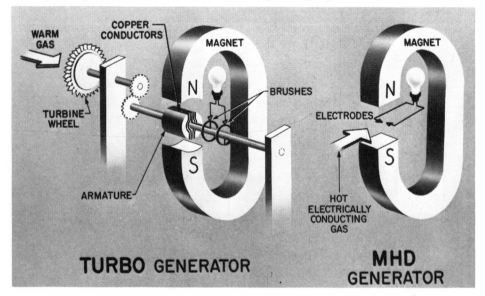

THE DIFFERENCE BETWEEN MHD *generators and conventional turbine-driven generators is shown here. Turbogenerator uses gas flow to turn a turbine that eventually spins a copper conductor in a magnetic field, thereby generating an electrical current. In the MHD generator, a hot, electrically conducting gas (actually a plasma) flows through a magnetic field and generates electricity directly.*

The steam turbine plant is the type that generates the overwhelming majority of the world's electrical power. It begins with a heat source, to boil water and make steam. The heat source can be a furnace that burns fossil fuel—coal, oil, natural gas—or the heat source could be a nuclear reactor. It's ironic that the most advanced source of energy that man's been able to develop, the energy of fissioning atoms, is used for nothing more glamorous than boiling water!

In a conventional power generator, then, we start with heat energy (fossil fuel or nuclear), which is converted to steam. The steam pushes the turbine blades. The mechanical energy of the turbine is then converted by the armature into electrical energy. The generator is thus an *energy conversion* device, converting heat energy into mechanical energy, and then mechanical energy into electrical energy.

Back to Faraday for a moment. Remember, he didn't discover merely that a copper armature rotating in a magnetic field will generate electricity. Most emphatically not. He made the much more profound discovery that *any* conductor of electricity moving relative to a magnetic field will generate electricity.

Plasmas are conductors of electricity.

The MHD Generator

Faraday understood the basic principles of MHD interactions. In fact, he tried to measure the electrical currents flowing in the River Thames. He reasoned that the river was fairly salty and therefore a reasonable conductor of electricity. And as it flowed to the sea, it was moving relative to the Earth's magnetic field. Could he measure the current that must be flowing through it?

The answer was a definite no. The Earth's magnetic field is much too weak, the flow of the river was too slow, and the conductivity of salty water far too low, to show a measurable current.

In an MHD generator, we'll see that three basic factors determine the performance of the generator: plasma conductivity, magnetic field strength, and the plasma's flow speed. MHD engineers would like to have all three as high as possible.

Although some plasmas are much better conductors than salt water, they're still far from the conductivities of most metals. The best man-made plasmas have conductivities that are several hundred thousand times lower than that of copper. However, plasmas can be made to move at supersonic speeds, and magnets can produce hundreds of thousands of gauss. And, as we'll see shortly, there's a trick that can greatly enhance the conductivity of a plasma, too.

If you move a plasma through a magnetic field, it's possible to generate an electrical current directly from the plasma. You can by-pass the whole mechanical system of turbines and armatures that conventional generators need. The MHD generator is called a *direct conversion* device: it converts heat energy directly to electricity without having a mechanical stage in between.

In principle, the MHD generator is quite simple. There are no mechanical moving parts, only the plasma moves. The MHD generator is basically a pipe, surrounded by a magnetic field coil. At one end of the pipe is a heat source; at the other end, an exhaust stack. Electrodes in the pipe tap off the current that's generated.

The MHD generator produces DC power only. Various schemes have been tried for making AC generators, but to date the simplest and cheapest way to produce AC is to convert the MHD generator's output in a conventional inverter.

Before we can understand how the MHD generator can be almost completely free of pollution, we must look at the generator itself more closely.

The plasma is produced in the heat source by simple *thermal ionization*. That is, the heat raises the temperature of the molecules to the point where electrons break free. The resulting plasma is only slightly ionized, even in the hottest burners available today. There are other ways to ionize a gas, such as using electrical fields or ultraviolet light to excite the electrons. In practical MHD generators, though, thermal ionization is the simplest and cheapest technique.

The plasma runs through the pipe—which we'll call the *MHD channel* from now on. The plasma is forced through the channel by simple gas pressure, much like the situation in a rocket nozzle. As we'll see throughout this chapter, there are many similarities between the MHD generator and rocket engines. In fact, the MHD generator can almost be thought of as a way to produce electricity from a rocket.

The magnetic field is arranged to run perpendicularly to the direction of the plasma flow. As Faraday showed, an electric current is generated in a direction that's perpendicular to both the magnetic field and the plasma flow.

Efficiency and problems

The MHD generator offers the possibility of much higher

efficiencies than turbogenerator power plants. The best steam turbogenerator plants are barely more than 40% efficient. Modern nuclear stations are less than 35% efficient. Calculations have shown that the first MHD power stations will be at least 50% efficient. Moreover, the MHD system will be open to further improvements. Conventional turbogenerators have been refined for nearly a century to reach their present-day level; it's doubtful that they'll be capable of any significant further improvement.

Even better, though, is the advantage of scaling. By its nature, the MHD generator becomes more efficient as its size increases. Losses in the MHD generator are mostly associated with the channel walls—friction between the walls and the flowing plasma, heat lost to the walls, electrode losses and other effects. The power output, on the other hand, is a product of the *volume* of the plasma in the channel. This means that as the size of an MHD generator increases, the losses rise with the square of the size (two-dimensional wall effects) while the power output rises with the cube of the size (three-dimensional volume effect). This "three-halves" relationship means that the bigger the generator, the better its efficiency.

Now look at thermal efficiency. All generators are essentially heat engines, and the amount of energy you can extract from them is directly related to the temperature difference between the hottest and coldest ends of the system. In engineering practice, this means that it's desirable to operate with as high a peak temperature as possible.

Turbines are limited in the peak temperature they can handle. If the gas blowing across the turbine blades is too hot, the blades will be destroyed. Despite the refinements of the toughest modern metal alloys and the best designs, turbines are still limited to operating temperatures well below 800°K (1000°F).

MHD generators operate today at top temperatures of about 3000°K. They can easily achieve peak temperatures beyond the fondest dreams of turbine engineers. This is both the great strength and main headache of MHD power generation.

For the MHD generator *needs* these very high temperatures. Unless the plasma fed into the generator is sufficiently ionized, its conductivity will be too low to allow the generator to work. And the easiest way to ionize a large continuous flow of gas is by heating it.

Still, most gases are very difficult to ionize by heating; the temperatures required are very high. Air, for example, must be heated to about 4500°K before a significant percentage of molecules start to shed their electrons. Conventional furnaces can't reach such a temperature.

The way around this problem was found by the American plasma physicist Richard J. Rosa (born 1927). While a graduate student at Cornell University, in the mid-1950's, he discovered that by adding a small amount of metallic material to a low-conductivity plasma, he could increase the conductivity to a point useful in MHD power generation. Rosa called this technique "seeding."

A burner operating at 3000°K can produce a plasma with sufficient conductivity for MHD if the combustion gas is "seeded" with a small amount of metallic powder. Potassium salts are commonly used as "seed" material in large MHD generators. In smaller machines, the more expensive metal cesium is often used. The reason behind the "seeding" technique is that the metals are ionized quite readily at temperatures where gases hardly ionize at all. So most of the free electrons in an MHD generator's plasma stream come from the metallic "seed."

While conventional burners can reach temperatures useful to MHD, nuclear reactors can't. This may seem strange, since the temperature within the fission elements of a reactor, where the atomic nuclei are splitting apart and releasing energy, must be astronomically high. But nuclear reactors are designed to run at low over-all temperature: less than 2000°K. If the metal casings that hold the fissionable material get much hotter than this, they may weaken or even break apart. This could cause destruction of the reactor (not necessarily an explosion) and might permit highly radioactive material to escape from the shielded reactor core.

Therefore, nuclear reactors can't deliver the high temperature needed for an MHD heat source. Higher-temperature reactors are being developed, and rocket reactors such as the ROVER nuclear rocket engine have reached temperatures useful for MHD, but only for a very short time. While nuclear reactors will probably be mated with MHD generators sometime in the future, it seems clear that the earliest MHD power plants will use furnaces that burn fossil fuel.

The Drive Toward MHD Power

Faraday understood the basics of MHD, and as early as 1910 several experimenters took out patents on various versions of an MHD generator. None of them were successful, mainly because their inventors couldn't heat the plasma to a temperature high enough for sufficient ionization.

In the late 1930's, Bela Karlovitz (born 1904) of the Westinghouse Research Laboratories built an MHD generator of considerable size and complexity. However, it also failed to work in a practical way. The science of plasma physics hadn't yet reached the point where the details of ionization and the dynamics of plasma interactions with magnetic fields were understood well enough to design a workable MHD generator.

In 1938, shortly after Bethe's announcement of the sun's energy source, Arthur Kantrowitz (born 1913) decided to study the problems of developing a fusion reactor. He was a gas physicist at the National Advisory Committee for Aeronautics facility in Langley, Virginia. NACA was to be revamped, twenty years later, into the National Aeronautics and Space Administration, NASA, the nation's space agency.

Kantrowitz's first attempts at building an experimental fusion reactor fell far short of approaching the conditions in the core of the sun, as he had expected. World War II forced an end to research, except for direct war-related work, and Kantrowitz devoted his efforts to jet-engine developments.

By 1949 he was an associate professor (and later full professor) at Cornell University. He began to try new ideas that might lead to a successful fusion reaction. The main problem was to produce a plasma of ultra-high temperature. Kantrowitz developed the shock tube as a laboratory apparatus for producing very high gas temperatures. A shock tube is a length of pipe in which a shock wave can be driven through the gas to be studied. The shock wave momentarily heats the gas to a very high temperature, in some cases high enough to ionize the gas significantly.

Kantrowitz soon realized that simple shock tubes wouldn't come close to producing fusion temperatures. But he also found that there were many intriguing things to investigate in gases that were heated "only" to 10,000°K or so.

"I was diverted from studying the fusion problem," he said in a conversation in 1970, "and I've been diverted from it ever since."

One of the causes of his diversion was his realization that practical MHD generators might be attainable.

Several fields of study gained tremendously during and after World War II. One of them, as we've seen, was plasma dynamics. In addition, the infant Space Age was starting to produce rocket

FIRST SUCCESSFUL MHD GENERATOR, *Avco's Mark I, produced slightly more than 10 kilowatts in 1958.*

burners and new materials that could stand up to the fiery heat of energetic plasmas.

Between 1950 and 1955, Kantrowitz and several of his graduate students at Cornell demonstrated that electrical power could be produced in a shock-tube model of an MHD generator. In 1955, these men left Cornell to establish the Avco Everett Research Laboratory, in Massachusetts. Their first objective wasn't MHD. The laboratory was set up to study the missile re-entry problem, and advise the Air Force as to whether or not a nose cone could be built to withstand the intense heat of re-entering the atmosphere at nearly 30,000 kilometers per hour.

Much of the work on the re-entry problem was also applicable to the plasma conditions inside an MHD generator. In 1958, Rosa built the first successful MHD generator. Called the Mark I, it produced slightly more than 10 kilowatts.

Although far from a practical power plant, the Mark I was an historic step. For the first time, a sizable amount of electrical power had been produced from a plasma. MHD power generation was a reality.

Britain, France, Russia, Japan, West Germany and several other nations quickly embarked on MHD development programs. In the United States, many industrial firms and Government and university laboratories started MHD studies. Among them were Atomics International, General Electric, Gulf General Atomic, Westinghouse, NASA's Jet Propulsion Laboratory, the Argonne National Laboratory (Atomic Energy Commission), Stanford University and the Massachusetts Institute of Technology. The Navy and Air Force both set up active research programs in MHD.

The largest and best-publicized program was put forward by Avco Corporation, under the leadership of Kantrowitz, and with the cooperation and financial support of a group of electric utility companies. Starting in 1959 they embarked on a program to develop practical MHD generators for utility power stations.

The Two Axis Approach

Their plan of attack involved developing two rather different kinds of experimental MHD equipment, and has been dubbed the "two axis" approach.

Under this plan, large high-power MHD generators were built to run for only a few seconds at a time. The basic aim of these tests was to determine how a plasma behaves under conditions such as a full-sized MHD power plant would require. For this purpose, running times of a few seconds are perfectly adequate, because the plasma attains equilibrium conditions within a second or so after the burner first turns on. That is, in about one second, the plasma has reached a steady-state condition. Its physical behavior will stay the same as long as the generator operates.

Avco's Mark II experimental MHD generator went into operation in 1961. It was designed to produce at least one megawatt (MW) of power output during run times of ten seconds. It eventually produced 1.5 MW. But more important, it produced enough

CHANNEL OF AN MHD GENERATOR *is built to contain supersonic flow of plasma at temperatures of thousands of degrees. This channel, for Avco's Mark V self-excited MHD generator, produced 32 megawatts of electrical output.*

experimental data so that engineers could begin designing bigger MHD generators with full confidence that they'd perform as predicted.

The success of the Mark II led to the eventual development of the Mark V self-excited MHD generator. The Mark V had more than ten times the power capability of the Mark II. Its channel could handle a total plasma flow of 130 pounds per second, compared to the 11 pounds per second of the Mark II. And the Mark V produced 32 MW of total power output. Yet in physical size, the Mark V was only slightly more than twice the Mark II's dimensions. This clearly showed the scaling advantages of the MHD generator.

The Mark V was a self-excited generator. That is, part of its gross power output was fed into the copper electromagnet, to keep it running. The magnet was started by power from a bank of batteries, but within a few seconds the MHD generator itself was powering the magnet. The copper magnet took about 10 MW of power, leaving better than 20 MW available as net power output.

The Department of Defense had sponsored development of the Mark V. Once it had proven itself, the Air Force contracted Avco to build a similar MHD generator at the Arnold Engineering Development Center (AEDC) in western Tennessee. This time, the MHD generator was no longer to be an experimental piece of apparatus. It was needed to do a specific job.

AEDC was developing a new type of wind tunnel, for testing advanced-design aircraft and spacecraft. The wind tunnel was nicknamed LORHO, which, translated from engineering jargon, meant that it was to be a wind tunnel that operates at low atmospheric density, capable of simulating the low densities found very high in the Earth's atmosphere. The Greek letter *rho* is an aerodynamicist's shorthand notation for gas density. Thus the low *rho* wind tunnel became LORHO.

The LORHO wind tunnel needed a burst of electrical power. The "pilot" facility, a small-scale model wind tunnel that would be used to check out the basic design concept, was going to need 20 MW for up to three minutes. The full-scale LORHO facility would need 600 MW. Buying bursts of power like that from the local utility was an unlikely possibility, even though the local utility was the low-cost, Federally-operated Tennessee Valley Authority (TVA). An electric power grid that's set up to provide constant power for homes and industry simply can't hand over 600 MW for a few minutes at a time, unless some very expensive special equipment is built into the system. And even then, the Air Force would have to run their wind tunnel at off-peak hours, such as between midnight and dawn.

An MHD generator is ideally suited to provide a short burst of high power. And, the Air Force realized, an MHD generator could be built right at the LORHO site and be completely self-contained. No need to bother anyone off-base, including TVA. So the "pilot" scale 20 MW LORHO generator was built, and has operated as designed.

While the Mark II, Mark V and LORHO generators tested the ability of MHD generators to deliver high powers, another type of MHD rig was providing answers about long running times.

Avco's Long Duration Test Facility (LDTF) was designed to test small MHD generators over time spans measured in months rather than minutes. These long duration tests were aimed at producing data on the MHD hardware and its ability to stand up to the high temperatures and other problems associated with high-speed flows of hot plasmas.

The MHD equipment tested in the LDTF was purposely kept small, since the costs of running larger hardware would be much higher. But even though the LDTF channels were limited to 10 kilowatts (kW) output power, the channels, electrodes, and other components had to face exactly the same temperatures, corrosion problems, and other plasma effects that a large-sized MHD generator faces.

The LDTF used a variety of fuels, including low-quality fuel oil and coal, types of fuels that are rarely used in conventional generators because of their corrosiveness and pollution products. MHD generator channels were tested for hundreds of hours, around the clock, without let-up. They showed no harmful effects. This evidence has led the engineers to believe that MHD generators will be able to use low-grade fuels that currently can't be used in conventional turbogenerator power stations.

A National MHD Program

By 1968, enough had been learned about the design and performance of MHD generators to prompt the Government into taking a serious look at this promising application of plasma technology.

The White House Science Advisor appointed a special panel to examine the progress and prospects for MHD power generation, and report their findings to the Office of Science and Technology.

In 1969, this panel, headed by Louis H. Roddis, Vice Chairman of the Consolidated Edison Company of New York, presented its report. Titled, "MHD for Central Station Power Generation: a Plan for Action," the report outlined a plan for a national program to develop full-scale MHD power generation stations. The report recommended a cooperative program involving the U.S. Department of the Interior, the nation's utility companies, and the industrial firms that are developing MHD generators.

MHD Power Plants

As MHD generators are developed and proved out at the high power outputs and long running times necessary for the electric utility companies, two major types of power plants will incorporate MHD generators into their design. In utility-company jargon, they're called the *peaking plant* and the *base-load plant*.

The peaking type of operation will probably be the first to use MHD. An MHD generator would be added on to a conventional turbogenerator plant, to be used only for short times, when a heavy demand for power is being felt. The word "peaking" thus has two meanings: it refers to the peak demand periods, the "rush hours" for electrical power; and it also refers to the fact that the MHD generator will use the peak temperature of the total system.

When the MHD generator "peaker" is in operation, it will produce tens or perhaps hundreds of megawatts of power. Its exhaust plasma, still very hot, will be used to boil water for the steam turbines in the rest of the plant. Thus the MHD generator adds to the total efficiency of the whole power station.

While the peaking plant can be thought of as a conventional steam turbine plant with an MHD generator attached in front, the base-load plant is more like an MHD generator system with a steam system tacked on behind. The base-load plant is the heart of

MHD STEAM POWER

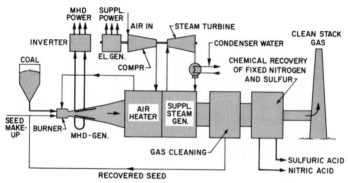

PLANT LAYOUT *for MHD-steam base load power station includes MHD generator, steam turbines, and pollution-cleaning systems.*

a utility's electrical system, the kind of plant that generates most of the system's power throughout the day and night. A base-load MHD plant would begin with an MHD generator. But since the exhaust from the MHD channel is still so hot and energetic, this exhaust will be used to make steam and generate still more electricity with conventional turbine equipment. The differences between the base-load plant and peaking plant are mainly those of size and aim. In the peaking plant, the MHD generator will probably be small and used only for a few hours per month. In the base-load plant, the MHD generator (though still small in physical dimensions) will produce at least half of the total plant's power output (500 MW or more). And the base load MHD generator will be designed to run for thousands of hours, continuously.

The best base-load plants of today, the fossil-fueled steam plants, are slightly better than 40% efficient. The earliest MHD base-load plant will be between 50% and 60% efficient. While we'll see shortly that this has important implications for pollution control, this increased efficiency of MHD also is vitally important to the economics of power generation. Cost studies of MHD power plants have shown that they'll be more economical to build than conventional or nuclear power stations. And the cost of electricity produced by MHD will be lower, a fact that should make both the utility owners and the bill-paying consumers smile with pleasure.

There's a third type of MHD system that might find possible use in the utilities' power grids: the emergency MHD generator.

The base-load plant is designed to operate for thousands of hours; the peaking plant will operate for a few hundred hours per year. An emergency MHD plant might operate for as little as a few hours, or even minutes, per year. But when it's needed it *must* perform.

The electric utilities are required by law to have a certain percentage of their total power generation capacity held in reserve. Each utility grid has several power stations that stand by, ready to come on the line with power if an emergency situation develops. The aim of this, of course, is to avert power shortages and blackouts. Of the reserve plants, some must be kept as "spinning reserve." That is, the boilers are hot, the turbines are spinning, and the generator can start producing electricity within a few minutes.

Spinning reserve is expensive. The utility must pay all the costs of having the generators operate without getting any electricity from them to sell. But spinning reserve is needed because it takes a steam turbine system much too long to come up to full power from a "cold start" to be of any help in a fast-developing emergency. Some emergencies have hit so quickly that even the spinning reserve wasn't on-line fast enough to prevent a blackout.

Moreover, as the increasing frequency of blackouts and brownouts has shown recently, the utilities' reserves are being stretched perilously thin. The demand for electrical power is growing much faster than new power stations can be built.

An emergency MHD generator could help to clear up this problem.

An MHD generator like the LORHO machine could sit totally shut down for months, then come on the line with its full power in a minute or less. Turning on an MHD generator is very much like turning on a rocket engine; within the time it takes the plasma to go through the channel, the MHD generator is putting out full power. The generator can remain idle, costing practically nothing until it's needed. Then it can come on the line with tens or hundreds of megawatts.

The difference between an emergency generator and a peaking unit isn't hard and fast. The economics of power generation may show it will be better for the utilities to build peaking MHD generators and have them available as emergency units when needed.

Pollution and Natural Resources

The MHD generator's advantages in pollution control, in conservation of natural resources, and in ecology can be summed up in a single word: efficiency.

Electric power stations make several kinds of pollution. There's

---

TABLE 4: COMPARISON OF STACK EMISSION FROM CONVENTIONAL STEAM POWER PLANTS AND MHD POWER PLANTS

Basis for Comparison:

Power Plant Capacity 1000 MW
Coal containing 3% sulfur burned with air

ESTIMATED POLLUTANTS EMISSION IN TONS PER DAY

	Conventional Steam	*MHD*
Particulate Matter	33	3
Sulfur Oxides (SO_2)	450	3
Nitrogen Oxides (NO_x)	80	4

---

thermal pollution of water. Steam power plants take in water from a stream or lake, use it to make steam, and then discharge the water back into its source at a temperature higher than it was originally. Fish, plants, and—most important—scavenging bacteria are often killed by being exposed to temperatures higher than they're accustomed to. In severe cases, the stream can be turned into a lifeless sewer. Nuclear power stations are even worse than fossil-fueled

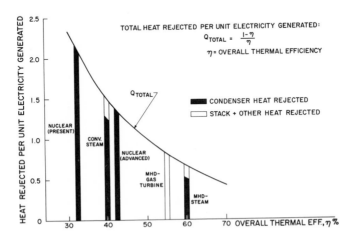

POLLUTION OUTPUT DEPENDS ON EFFICIENCY *of power generator. Graph shows that the more-efficient MHD systems will produce relatively little heat pollution. MHD generator with gas turbines can be designed to produce no thermal pollution of water at all. MHD-steam combination is lowest in overall heat pollution.*

plants when it comes to thermal pollution of water, because they operate at lower efficiencies, and thus have more heat to reject.

Then there's the familiar *air pollution* of the fossil-fueled station's belching smokestacks. The nuclear plants are quite clean when it comes to air pollution. But the exhaust products of the combustion that takes place in the fossil plants' burners foul our air with unsightly and unhealthy soot, carbon monoxide, and oxides of sulfur and nitrogen.

The big, ugly dark clouds coming out of the stacks are an obvious eyesore. But the invisible gaseous compounds such as the oxides of nitrogen are probably more dangerous, harder to identify, and much harder to get rid of. The sulfur oxides can be controlled to some extent by using fuels that are low in sulfur content.

There's a third type of pollution that's connected only with nuclear generator: radioactivity. While there's been much strong public reaction to the potential hazards from radioactivity, there seems to be much less danger of a nuclear reactor exploding or accidentally letting a harmful amount of radioactivity loose than the dangers from air and water pollution.

Thermal pollution is nothing more than waste heat. The higher a generator's efficiency, the more of the energy originally in its fuel will come out as electricity, and the less waste heat there'll be. While no machine is going to be 100% efficient, the MHD generator will be half-again as efficient as the best modern turbine systems. This means less waste heat, per kilowatt-hour of electricity generated.

Moreover, it will be possible to develop MHD power stations that require no steam cycle at all. Instead of feeding the MHD generator's exhaust into steam boilers and steam turbines, jet-engine type gas turbines can be built into the MHD station instead. Without the necessity for steam, the power station can run without drawing any water whatsoever, except the slight amount needed as a coolant in various parts of the machinery. But the coolant can be kept in a "closed loop" and recycled continuously without drawing fresh water from outside the plant or rejecting heated water.

An MHD-gas turbine station would still generate waste heat, and in fact may be slightly less efficient than an MHD-steam system. But the waste heat from a gas-turbine cycle would be rejected to the atmosphere, not to a natural water source. In many parts of the United States, where water is scarce and can't be used as a dumping pool for waste heat, the MHD-gas turbine station offers perhaps the only way of developing large power stations. And the heat that's to be rejected to the atmosphere might be used in other ways, too. There's still some energy in that exhaust gas; some enterprising engineer will probably come up with a scheme for turning it into useful work.

The same efficiency that keeps thermal pollution low in an MHD generator will also tend to help reduce air pollution. If you get more kilowatts per pound of fuel, you can use less fuel to get the power you want, and thus produce less air pollution.

But the exhaust of an MHD generator is loaded with pollutants, just the same. In fact, it's so bad that it's good! There's more of the oxides of nitrogen and sulfur in an MHD exhaust than in a conventional generator's smokestack (assuming that the MHD station is burning low grade, sulfur-rich fuels). And the MHD exhaust contains an extra pollutant that conventional machines don't have: the potassium "seed" material that was injected into the burner to enhance the plasma's conductivity.

The seed material and the high temperature of the exhaust plasma are the two keys to controlling the MHD generator's air pollution.

First, the potassium seed is valuable. To make MHD economically attractive as possible, it's necessary to recover the seed rather than let it escape out of the stack. So, built into the MHD station is an efficient particle separator that will shake all the particulate material out of the exhaust gases. The potassium will be recovered and recycled. All the soot and fly-ash and other pollution particles will be trapped before they get into the air outside the station.

Removal of the oxides of nitrogen and sulfur is a bit trickier, but much more elegant.

As the plasma comes out of the MHD generator channel it is loaded with these oxides. But the temperature of the MHD exhaust is very high, high enough to allow some interesting chemical reactions to take place. If the exhaust gases are put through an expanding nozzle, like a rocket nozzle, the gases will quickly cool down to the point where the nitrogen and sulfur oxides can be removed from the gas stream by well-known chemical separation techniques. Experiments have shown that this can be done, while still not cooling the exhaust so much that it becomes useless for steam or gas turbines. And the nitrogen and sulfur oxides so recovered can be sold for fertilizer production!

So recovering the potassium seed and nitrogen and sulfur oxides helps both the economics of the MHD station and leads to a final exhaust gas that contains little more than harmless carbon dioxide, molecular nitrogen, and water vapor.

In this discussion of MHD and pollution, we've assumed that MHD power stations will use conventional furnaces and burn fossil fuels. As we'll see shortly, the possibility of practical nuclear-MHD stations isn't out of the question, but certainly appears further downstream than fossil-fueled MHD generators.

The MHD generator will be able to burn fuels that can't be used in steam turbine plants. In essence, the MHD system will help to save our existing supply of coal, oil and natural gas, by using low grades of coal and oil that are currently considered unfit for use.

There are several reasons for this. First, the MHD generator system can trap the sulfur oxides in its exhaust and even make commercial use out of them. This means that MHD stations can burn high-sulfur coal without causing increased air pollution. Steam turbine plants can't do this, and right now many of this nation's coal reserves are lying idle and unused.

Also, the MHD generator can handle highly corrosive fuels without trouble, which turbines can't do. Again, this means that fuel reserves now being ignored can be utilized to produce useful electrical power. It could also mean new jobs and new dignity for the people of the depressed coal-mining regions of our nation.

And the possibilities of building MHD-gas turbine systems that need little or no water can have enormous implications for the western regions of the United States, and all other water-poor areas of the world.

In many western states there are huge deposits of low-grade coal and virtually no water available for industrial use. MHD power plants can use that coal and don't need water. Cheap, abundant electrical power could attract new industry to regions that are now depressed. New towns and cities could be built, perhaps, based on rational planning and new technology. The flow of people from the countryside into our already overcrowded and decaying older cities might be checked in this way.

A fanciful dream, maybe. But it's fascinating to think that the softly-glowing plasma in Crooke's discharge tubes of a century ago might have such important implications for the nation and the world before this century is finished.

MHD in Other Nations

The prospects of MHD power generation have attracted great interest in many nations. In some cases, the major attraction is that MHD will reduce the costs of fuel for power generation. To nations like Japan, France and Britain, which import almost all their fuel and consequently have very high fuel costs, MHD offers a way toward much cheaper electricity. And more of it.

For other nations that are trying to build up their industrial capacity very rapidly, MHD offers a way to generate large amounts of electricity with high efficiency, using almost any available fuel. The MHD program in Russia, for example, seems aimed primarily at producing abundant electricity, with the expense probably coming second in the minds of the Soviet planners.

The Russian program is probably the largest national effort in the world in MHD, as of this moment. Three major scientific and technical groups are involved in it: the Institute of High Temperature, the Kurchatov Atomic Energy Institute, and the Krzhyanovsky Power Engineering Institute. At the Institute of High Temperature, a 75 MW MHD-steam power station is being developed, to serve as a "pilot model" for a full-scale MHD-steam station. Known as the U-25, this pilot plant will produce 25 MW from its MHD generator and the remainder from the steam turbines. Natural gas will be used as the fuel. Studies of other MHD systems, coal burning and nuclear powered, are being carried out at other sites.

The Japanese are actively pursuing MHD power systems based both on fossil fuels (oil, for the most part) and on nuclear energy. The Japanese programs are supported both by their government and by private industry. In 1969 the Japanese announced that they had successfully operated an MHD generator with a superconducting magnetic field coil.

Superconducting magnets are one of the technical miracles of the 1960's. If they're kept at ultra-low *cryogenic* temperatures, they can produce extremely strong magnetic fields with no need for electrical power at all after they're turned on. While no one expected unusual difficulties in mating superconducting magnets with MHD generators, the Japanese are the first to do so, and to demonstrate that the near-absolute-zero magnet can work while a 3000°K plasma is streaming just a few centimeters away from it. The advantages of superconducting magnets, and some of their problems, will be briefly discussed at the end of this chapter.

Like all of science and technology, MHD knows no national boundaries. And, thankfully, the world's MHD scientists and engineers have been cooperating with each other to a considerable extent. There are several international MHD conferences which draw participants from all over the world.

Nuclear MHD Systems

To an MHD generator, a nuclear reactor is simply another heat source. But in the practical world, a nuclear-MHD combination holds many very desirable attractions.

MHD can increase the efficiency and decrease the thermal pollution of nuclear power stations. Conversely, nuclear reactors can provide MHD generators with a vast new fuel source that they can't draw upon right now.

As we've seen earlier, most nuclear reactors don't put out a high enough temperature for MHD power generation. Exhaust temperatures of nuclear reactors are gradually rising, although there's still a long way to go. The gap might never be bridged, simply because of the safety problems of nuclear reactors. But there's another way to span the gap: MHD engineers can find ways to operate their generators at lower temperatures.

One possibility is to find a method of reducing the high-temperature requirement of the MHD generator's plasma. The second route is to avoid the plasma problem altogether and use a liquid metal as the working fluid in the MHD generator.

We don't ordinarily think of metals in the liquid state, but mercury is a liquid at room temperature (70°F, 25°C, 298°K). Metals such as sodium and potassium can be liquefied at temperatures of only 371°K and 337°K, respectively. And these fluids have the conductivities of metals, not plasmas. On the other hand, liquid metals present many materials problems, since they tend to be both corrosive and sticky. They're difficult to pump and hard to move through a generator. But much research is being done on nuclear-MHD systems using liquid metals, particularly in laboratories of NASA and the Atomic Energy Commission. As we'll see in the next chapter, a nuclear-MHD power generator using liquid metals may be a very useful power source for a spacecraft.

Plasma physicists are also working toward useful nuclear-MHD systems that use a plasma as the working fluid. It's clear, though, that thermal ionization can't be counted on at the low temperatures expected from nuclear reactors. *So extra-thermal ionization* techniques are being investigated.

We saw in Chapter 4 that the high temperatures in the sun's corona are due to extra-thermal forces; in the corona, Alfvén waves are pumping energy into the plasma particles. Here on Earth, in several laboratories, various techniques are being tried to induce extra-thermal ionization in man-made plasmas. The basic aim is to produce a plasma in which the electrons are much more energetic than the remainder of the plasma. This is called a *non-equilibrium* plasma, because the electron temperature is no longer in equilibrium with the temperature of the ions and neutral particles. If the electrons can be raised to a high enough temperature, the conductivity of the plasma will be sufficient to allow MHD effects to take place, even though the bulk of the plasma is at a relatively low temperature.

To date, several research teams have produced non-equilibrium plasmas, but not under conditions that would be useful in a practical MHD generator. Usually, the electron temperature is still too low to produce useful conductivity, even though the temperature of the rest of the plasma is even lower.

But the search goes on. For a nuclear-driven MHD generator promises to be the best power source, with the lowest costs for electricity, that man can develop—unless (or until) a practical fusion reactor is made to work.

Postscript on Superconducting Magnets

You recall that when we discussed the Avco Mark V self-excited

SUPERCONDUCTING MAGNET, *one of the world's largest, was built by Avco Everett Research Laboratory in mid-1960's to test design of superconducting field coils for MHD generator power stations. This coil is about one-third actual size required for power station.*

MHD generator, we pointed out that 10 MW of the generator's power went into feeding the copper magnet. From an economic point of view, a power generator would be much better off if its magnet didn't need any electricity. There are natural magnets, such as lodestones, but they're much too low in field strength to be used in any practical large-sized power generators.

In 1960, researchers at the Bell Telephone Laboratories announced the discovery of something that seemed miraculous: a combination of materials that produced a magnet capable of nearly 100,000 gauss *yet didn't need any electrical power input* once it was energized. This was the first high-field-strength *superconducting* magnet.

Superconductivity had been known since 1911. Certain materials such as mercury lose all their electrical resistance when they're cooled down to a temperature near absolute zero. Such temperatures are called *cryogenic,* from the Greek *kryos,* which means "icy cold." The superconductors discovered in 1911 were capable of only rather modest magnetic field strengths, and were useful only as scientific curiosities.

But the superconducting materials discovered in the 1960's are capable of sustaining fields of from 30,000 to 400,000 gauss! These materials are all compounds or alloys of metals such as niobium, zirconium, tin, titanium, and a few others.

When an electrical current is put into a superconductor, the current remains circulating through the material continuously, with no measurable resistance. So you can charge up a superconducting magnet and then disconnect the electrical power. The magnet will remain energized indefinitely, as long as it stays superconducting.

To remain superconducting, the material must be kept at a cryogenic temperature. Usually liquid helium is used to refrigerate superconductors. Helium liquefies at 4.2°K. Most superconductors lose their superconducting properties at temperatures of between 10°K and 20°K.

Like all new discoveries, there were a number of practical problems associated with superconductors. But most of these have been solved, and large, reliable superconducting magnets are being built today even though the exact details of the physics of superconductivity aren't yet clearly understood.

For the MHD generator, superconducting magnets are a godsend. First, they need no power. Second, they produce much higher field strengths than room-temperature electromagnets, and MHD generators can capitalize on high field strength more than conventional generators can.

SIX

Plasmas for Space Flight

Man has set out on the road of space exploration. He's walked on the Moon and lived for weeks at a time in orbit around the Earth. Unmanned satellites observe our planet's weather, relay radio and television broadcasts, and do other tasks of increasing importance to our global society. Robot spacecraft have gone to Mars and Venus, probing their mysteries for the inquisitive men of Earth.

Space flight today is in much the same stage as aviation was in 1910. We know spacecraft can be made to work, and they're tremendously exciting. They offer the prospect of changing our outlook on the universe, and thus changing our society. But, at the moment, they're almost prohibitively expensive. Only the very richest nations can afford large programs of space exploration. Before the promise of space flight can bring real benefits of knowledge to mankind, before space flight can be anything but a rich nation's hobby, we must find more efficient, cheaper ways of transporting men and equipment through space. After all, air travel didn't begin to affect the way he lived and did business until long-range aircraft became efficient enough, and ticket prices cheap enough, to allow almost everyone to fly whenever and wherever he wanted to.

There are four main objectives ahead of us in space. First, both manned and unmanned satellites can help to do things that will improve the quality of life here on Earth. Global communications and weather observation from orbit are already being done. Satellites can also be used to help in locating natural resources, such as oil; in checking on the health of croplands and forests; in spotting forest fires while they're still small enough to control; in mapping pollution patterns; in pinpoint navigation for ships and planes—the list goes on and on.

Second, there's an entire world to be explored: the Moon. Third, men want to set foot on Mars, and to explore both Mars and Venus as thoroughly as possible. Fourth, unmanned spacecraft can probe all the other planets of our solar system.

All of these objectives could be accomplished by the turn of the century. But only the first one can be done easily by existing rocket boosters and spacecraft equipment. To fully explore the Moon, to reach Mars, to probe the other planets—we'll need rockets that can carry more payload more cheaply and efficiently than anything we have now.

Plasma technology can help to make those rockets. In fact, plasma technology has already helped to make today's succesful space flights possible. And any progress in space flight hardware is going to depend critically on plasma scientists and engineers.

The Re-entry Problem

The first problem that plasma dynamics helped to solve dealt with the end of a space flight: the re-entry of a spacecraft or missile nose cone into the atmosphere. Coming in from space at speeds of six to 12 kilometers per second, a re-entering space vehicle resembles a blazing meteor. Most meteoroids are completely destroyed before they reach the ground. The problem facing missile and spacecraft designers in the mid-1950's was to develop re-entry vehicles that could survive temperatures of 10,000°K or more—hotter than the surface of the sun.

When a re-entry vehicle dips back into the atmosphere at such high speed, it creates a shock wave that heats the air around the vehicle to incandescence. The air literally glows as molecules of oxygen and nitrogen are ripped apart into individual atoms, and even ionized to an appreciable extent. The spacecraft is surrounded by a blazing shell of partially-ionized plasma. The heat from this plasma could destroy a poorly designed or poorly controlled vehicle. The electrical conductivity of the plasma sheath around the vehicle cuts off radio communications with the ground during the most dangerous few moments of re-entry.

Scientists and engineers tackled the re-entry problem by studying shock-heated air in shock tubes. As we saw in Chapter 5, a pioneer in using the shock tube for producing and studying high-temperature gases was Arthur Kantrowitz.

The shock tube is an unglamorous-looking piece of pipe. Some of the largest shock tubes are as wide as 60 centimeters in diameter and 30 meters long. The tube is divided into two sections: a short driver section, and a test section that takes up most of the tube's length. The test section is filled with the gas to be studied, under the conditions of interest to the researchers. In the early re-entry investigations, the test gas was air at the low density to be found high in the Earth's atmosphere.

The driver section is separated from the test section by a thin metal diaphragm. The pressure in the driver section is increased by any of several methods to the point where the diaphragm bursts. The high-pressure driver gas suddenly pushes into the test gas, setting up a shock wave that rushes down the length of the tube in a fraction of a second. The shock wave violently compresses and heats the gas, simulating the conditions created when a re-entry vehicle roars through the upper atmosphere.

Shock-tube studies quickly showed how much heat would be produced in air by a re-entering vehicle's shock wave. Engineers then began to design re-entry vehicles that could withstand such heating. But two problems arose: (1) wind tunnel testing of re-entry vehicles and their heat shield materials; and (2) the radio blackout caused by the re-entry plasma sheath.

Both problems were attacked by plasma researchers.

Ordinary wind tunnels simply can't produce the very-high-temperature gas flow needed to test the heat shield of a re-entry vehicle. The shock tube can produce the proper gas conditions, but only for a fraction of a second. The answer to this problem was the development of a new type of wind tunnel, where the air is heated by an electrical arc—a sort of continuous, man-made stroke of lightning. The resulting apparatus is called the *plasma-arc-jet* wind tunnel.

Most plasma-arc-jet wind tunnels are small, too small to test a full-sized re-entry vehicle. The electrical power needed to create

PLASMA ARC JET *uses electrical energy to create hot stream of plasma. Plasma arcs have been used both for testing materials such as spacecraft heat shields, and as electrical rockets for space missions.*

enough high-temperature plasma to spray over a full-sized APOLLO command module, for example, would be enough to light a good-sized city. Instead, the engineers test smaller models of re-entry vehicles and, more importantly, they test samples of the heat shield materials. These small-scale tests are later checked out on un-manned test flights of the full-sized vehicles. The plasma-arc-jet wind-tunnel tests have given detailed information on the performance of the vehicles and heat shields; the data they produce are accepted with full confidence.

The plasma arc jet has turned out to be useful in many other applications, too, applications that have little to do with space exploration.

In the guise of the *plasma torch* it's used to cut metals in steel foundries and shipyards. In Russia, plasma torches have been used to help drill oil wells through solid rock; the star-hot plasma cracks even the hardest rocks. And *plasma spray guns* have been developed to spray metals and ceramic materials quickly and evenly over almost any surface. The heat-shield material for the APOLLO command module, for example, was sprayed onto the spacecraft's metal honeycomb structure by plasma spray guns. Many scientists are now studying some of the chemical reactions that can be created by a 10,000°K plasma torch. There appear to be many new industrial applications for plasma arc jets, and the technology of the 1970's and 1980's will see increasing use of this versatile tool.

The second problem of re-entry—the plasma-caused radio blackout—is still unsolved. For a few moments during every re-entry flight, communications with the re-entering spacecraft are lost because radio waves can't penetrate the plasma sheath that surrounds the spacecraft during the hottest portion of its flight. Several methods have been tried to get around this problem, including dumping materials into the plasma that will absorb electrons and thus lower the plasma's conductivity. None of these techniques has worked well enough to become practical. The radio blackout is still there. It's annoying, but doesn't appear to be dangerous.

On the other hand, the plasma sheath presents a brilliant radar target, and makes tracking a re-entering vehicle quite easy. This is especially important in spotting missile nose cones, and the Anti-Ballistic Missile (ABM) system's radars take advantage of this.

Re-entry scientists and engineers are now looking into the problems of landing on other planets.

Mars is a cold dry, almost airless planet. Its atmospheric pressure at ground level is roughly equal to the air pressure on Earth at an altitude of 30,000 meters—high above the stratosphere. Even if Mars' atmosphere were pure oxygen, it would be too thin for a man to breathe. Landing a spacecraft on Mars will be almost like landing on the airless Moon; the atmosphere won't be much help in slowing the spacecraft; on the other hand, there won't be much of a heating problem caused by the Martian atmosphere.

Venus presents just the opposite picture. Earth's so-called sister planet has a thick, hot atmosphere that destroyed the first two Russian VENERA spacecraft that penetrated into it. The atmospheric pressure at ground level has been estimated to be at least ten times greater than Earth's sea-level pressure, and the temperatures on the ground can soar to 700°K—nearly hot enough to melt aluminum. There's water vapor in Venus' atmosphere, in the brilliant white clouds that eternally hide the planet's surface from our view. But down at ground level, Venus must be a red-hot oven. It will be very difficult to design unmanned vehicles that can land intact and survive there. Manned flights to Venus' surface seem to be very far off.

Looking farther afield, the planet Mercury seems to have no atmosphere at all, or at best such a thin one that landing a spacecraft there will be similar to landing on the Moon. And although Mercury is the closest planet to the sun, its highest surface temperature appears to be about 600°K, slightly lower than hothouse Venus.

Going outward from the sun, beyond Mars are Jupiter and the other gas giant planets. No one knows if these planets have any solid surfaces at all. All we see of them is swirling layers of clouds. Jupiter is about 11 times larger than Earth, and its gravitational field at the cloud surface is more than twice our ground-level gravity. Beneath the clouds, the atmospheric pressure quickly builds to titanic values, far higher than anything found in the deepest parts of the oceans on Earth. Manned flights to Jupiter will no doubt be restricted to landings on some of the twelve known Jovian moons. Unmanned spacecraft may dip into Jupiter's clouds, but even plasma technology can offer no means to protect a human crew against the killing pressures of Jupiter's atmosphere and gravity.

Radiation Shielding

When we start thinking about manned missions to the planets, we must consider the problem of radiation dangers.

As we saw in Chapter 4, the weather in space can kill an unprotected astronaut. The primary danger comes from strong solar flares, with the bursts of high-energy protons that they hurl out through the solar system. While proton energies sometimes reach thousands of BeV, the average energy of flare-emitted protons is in the range of a few hundred MeV, which is still powerful enough to penetrate several centimeters of lead.

Satellites orbiting within Earth's magnetosphere are protected from most of the dangers of flare radiation. But missions to the Moon and planets must leave Earth's magnetic umbrella behind them and venture out into the sometimes-dangerous weather in space.

The APOLLO spacecraft wasn't shielded against the radiation of strong flares. The APOLLO missions are timed to avoid major flares. While it's not yet possible to predict the eruption of a solar flare with the accuracy of terrestrial weather forecasts, astronomers can watch for very active sunspot groups. Since flares are usually born in such sunspot activity, lunar flights are generally timed to avoid periods when very active sunspots could give rise to a dangerous flare. Since the flight time to the Moon is only a few days, and major flares generally happen weeks or even months apart, solar flares haven't yet interfered with lunar missions.

If a strong flare should erupt while astronauts are on the Moon, they could protect themselves by digging an underground shelter. A few centimeters of lunar soil should stop most of the harmful radiation. Since the high-energy protons take at least twelve hours to reach the Earth's vicinity, the astronauts would have enough time to protect themselves. If the flare came while the astronauts were in flight between the Earth and Moon, though, they could very easily be killed by the radiation.

On the long flights to Mars and the other planets, missions that will take months or years of flight time, the astronauts will be exposed to many flares. The spacecraft's skin and the shielding effect of the equipment inside the craft can protect the astronauts against some radiation, but the multi-hundred-MeV protons pose a lethal danger to planetary mission crews.

Manned spacecraft going to the planets will need some form of radiation shielding. They'll be in space long enough to encounter several major flares.

The simplest type of shielding is a solid wall, like the lead shields around x-ray machines. But solid shields are heavy. To protect a three-man crew in a cabin slightly smaller than the APOLLO command module against 200 MeV protons, nearly two tons of shielding are needed. It might be possible to design "storm cellars" inside a large spacecraft, perhaps deep within the fuel tanks, and use the spacecraft skin and the fuel itself for shielding. But the storm cellar will still need thick, heavy walls to be sure of stopping the energetic protons.

Another approach is to use "active" shielding. Instead of carrying a solid shield to passively absorb protons, an active shield would deflect the particles away from the spacecraft, or at least slow them down to the point where they wouldn't be harmful if they penetrated the spacecraft's interior.

When high-field-strength superconducting magnets were announced in the early 1960's, several scientists and engineers got the idea that a superconducting magnet could make an effective radiation shield for a spacecraft. Superconducting magnets, at field strengths of 100,000 gauss or better, would be able to deflect all but the most energetic protons away from the spacecraft. Best of all, superconducting magnets don't need a continuous supply of electrical energy, once they're charged up. The heavy electrical power supply that ordinary magnets need can stay on the ground.

The idea seemed to make beautiful sense. After all, the Earth is protected by its magnetosphere; why not create miniature magnetospheres around spacecraft to protect them? Calculations quickly showed that a superconducting magnet strong enough to protect against protons up to several hundred MeV would weigh far less than a solid radiation shield. And while the more energetic protons would get through to the spacecraft, there are so few of them that they don't pose as serious a radiation threat as the more numerous 100 to 500 MeV protons.

But the calculations also showed a fatal flaw in the idea. At field strengths of 100,000 gauss or more, the superconducting magnet is exerting titanic bending stresses on itself. All magnets stress themselves, and very powerful magnets on Earth are often buttressed by steel retaining structures that hold the magnet together. But the superconducting magnet would tear itself apart unless supported by a formidable retaining structure, and when all the numbers were added up, it turned out that the superconducting radiation shield was just about as heavy as a solid, passive shield. No significant advantage.

In the meantime, other investigators had been looking into the possibility of using electrostatic forces to deflect high-energy protons from a spacecraft. The idea here was to charge the outer wall of the spacecraft to a very high positive electrical charge, many millions of volts (megavolts). The incoming protons would "see" a very strong positive charge, and since like electrical charges repel each other, the protons would be deflected from the spacecraft. But there are also electrons in space, and they'd be attracted to the spacecraft. The electrons would quickly neutralize the high positive charge, and the electrostatic shield would disappear. To keep the spacecraft properly charged up, it would be necessary to get rid of electrons continuously, by running electrical equipment that would take up as much weight, or more, as a solid radiation shield. Again, this type of active shielding offered no practical advantage over a passive shield.

But there is an idea, born in plasma physics, that offers hope of a truly lightweight, effective active radiation shield. Called the *plasma radiation shield,* it combines some of the features of both magnetic and electrostatic shielding, plus a knowledge of plasma behavior.

Basically, the plasma radiation shield uses electrostatic forces to deflect the incoming protons, and magnetic forces to keep the electrons away from the spacecraft.

The spacecraft is charged to a high positive potential, perhaps as much as 200 megavolts. This will deflect protons of about 200 MeV, and absorb so much energy from the stronger protons that they'd be relatively harmless by the time they'd fought their way through the electrostatic shield and the spacecraft's metal skin.

To keep the electrons off the spacecraft, a relatively weak super-conducting magnet is used. This magnet needn't face up to the job of holding off high-energy protons; it merely has to keep the much-less-energetic electrons away from the craft's skin. If the electrons are kept away from the spacecraft, then the high positive charge can be maintained indefinitely without the need for a constant supply of high-power electricity.

The spacecraft is surrounded, then, by a cloud of electrons held off by the lightweight superconducting magnet. The incoming pro-tons are so energetic that they fly right through the electron cloud as if it didn't exist. They're repelled, though, by the 200-megavolt charge on the spacecraft and are deflected away from the spacecraft.

It's been estimated that a plasma radiation shield for an APOLLO-sized capsule would weigh only a few hundred kilo-grams, and for larger vehicles its weight advantage over solid shielding is even stronger. However, there's much to be learned about the behavior of the electron cloud that would gather around the spacecraft, and the way it would interact with the lower-energy protons that it will encounter. The electron cloud might be un-stable, and there might be other effects that would make the plasma radiation shield concept impractical.

But it would be poetically fitting if plasma technology provides the protection needed to shield against plasma-caused radiation dangers in space.

When we're ready to travel out to Mars, Venus, and the farther planets, plasma technology will be with us. It seems clear, right now, that plasma rockets of very high efficiency will make manned interplanetary voyages possible.

Electrical Propulsion

In a sense, all rockets are plasma engines. The exhaust bellow-ing from today's rocket booster is a weakly-ionized plasma.

The energy that propels these boosters is simple chemical energy, from combustion. A rocket engine burns propellants to create a high-temperature gas (or plasma). The rocket nozzle allows the exhaust to escape in one direction. Newton's third law of motion predicts correctly that an equal and opposite force will push the booster in the opposite direction.

Chemical rockets have started us on the road of space exploration. Men have ridden them to the Moon. But chemical rockets are notoriously inefficient, and it's doubtful that space exploration will be anything other than an expensive hobby, unless more efficient rocket engines are developed. After all, if explorers such as Columbus, Hudson, Balboa, *et al* had to throw away most of their ships each time they sailed, and returned home in tiny rowboats, the New World might never have been settled.

To understand the shortcomings of chemical rockets, and how plasma rockets might help overcome these problems, we must take a brief look at the basics of rocket propulsion.

Rocket engines provide *thrust*, the force that works against inertia. When a booster lifts off, the thrust of its engines works directly against the Earth's gravity. If the thrust is greater than the booster's weight, the vehicle rises off the ground. In orbit, where the spacecraft is effectively weightless, it still takes thrust to change speed, to move from one orbit to another, to break free of orbit altogether.

The thrust that a rocket engine can deliver depends on two factors: the amount of plasma flowing out of the nozzle, and the velocity with which the plasma leaves the nozzle. (The material going through the nozzle needn't be plasma, it can be anything. But in most rockets, the matter fired through the nozzle is in the plasma state.)

If you think about it a moment, you can see that the best way to make a rocket engine efficient is to use as small an amount of propellant plasma as possible, and to make the exhaust velocity of the plasma as high as possible.

Rocket engineers have a term for the efficiency of a rocket engine: it's called *specific impulse*. The specific impulse of a rocket engine is determined by the ratio of thrust compared to the rate at which the propellant is used up:

$$\text{Specific impulse} = \frac{\text{thrust}}{\text{propellant flow rate}}$$

Since thrust is measured in kilograms, and the propellant flow rate in kilograms per second, specific impulse is always expressed in seconds. It can be thought of as the length of time that a kilogram of propellant (fuel and oxidizer) will give a kilogram of thrust.

Chemical rockets are limited to specific impulses of less than 400 seconds, and exhaust velocities of some 4000 meters per second. These appear to be the best performance figures available by burning a chemical fuel and oxidizer.

In the chemical rocket, both the basic energy and the thrust are provided by the propellants themselves. But there are other possibilities. For example, a propellant could be heated without being burned. A nuclear reactor could act as the heat source.

In this type of rocket, the energy source is separate from the propellant. Hydrogen would make a good propellant here, because it's the lightest element and thus the easiest to accelerate. It takes less energy to accelerate a hydrogen atom or molecule to a given velocity than any other element's atoms or molecules. NASA and the Atomic Energy Commission have been developing such *nuclear thermal rockets* under the NERVA program. They have produced an experimental nuclear rocket called *Rover,* which will achieve a specific impulse of about 1000 seconds and an exhaust velocity of some 8000 meters per second.

The nuclear thermal rocket, then, can give twice the exhaust velocity and two-and-a half times the efficiency of the best chemical rockets. But there are other types of rockets that might be even better.

In the nuclear thermal rocket, it's still heat energy that accelerates the propellant. And there are limits to how much heat a propellant can usefully accept; after a certain temperature is reached, more heat energy doesn't produce more thrust. Also, there are limits on how much heat the metals of the reactor, the rocket nozzle, and the propellant piping can stand.

Under the proper conditions, electromagnetic energy can accelerate a propellant. There's an entire family of *electrical rockets,* and they've shown themselves capable of producing specific impulses of much more than 10,000 seconds.

High specific impulse means high efficiency, but electrical rockets suffer from two important drawbacks. First, they need sizable power supplies, on the order of 100 kilowatts per kilogram of thrust. Secondly, they produce very low thrusts. Where chemical rockets such as those of the SATURN V booster produce nearly 3000 *tons* of thrust, electric rockets produce a few grams at most. They're efficient, but very low-powered.

Electric rockets can't be used to boost a vehicle off the ground, they simply don't deliver enough thrust. Boosters will continue to use chemical rockets for the foreseeable future. Nuclear thermal rockets might be able to deliver enough thrust for ground-to-orbit boosting, but their exhausts are going to be radioactive. For that reason, nuclear thermal rockets will be restricted to uses well beyond Earth's atmosphere.

Once a spacecraft's in orbit, though, it's virtually weightless. Even a very low thrust will accelerate it. And if the thrust can be applied over a long period of time, the spacecraft will eventually reach a very high speed. This is the province of electrical rockets.

It's like the difference between a weightlifter and a safari porter. The weightlifter may be able to pick up a heavy load, but how far can he carry it? The chemical rockets will put spacecraft in orbit; from there, the quiet, efficient electrical rockets will carry the load for the long distances.

Chemical rockets, with their high thrust but low efficiency, must accelerate a spacecraft very quickly, within a few minutes. Then the spacecraft coasts through frictionless space toward its destination. This is rather like throwing a baseball: all the impulse is applied at the beginning of the flight, and the rest of the time is spent coasting.

But an electrical rocket can keep running for days, or weeks, or months, constantly accelerating the spacecraft, propelling faster and faster for each second that the engine operates.

For missions from the Earth to the Moon or the nearer planets, chemical rockets can provide faster flight times than electrical rockets. The SATURN/APOLLO vehicle takes a few days from the Earth to the Moon. An electrical rocket with a specific impulse of 5000 seconds but a thrust of only 0.07 kilogram would need 150 days to go from an orbit around the Earth to an orbit around the Moon. But while the SATURN/APOLLO needs 100 kilograms of booster weight for each kilogram of payload, the electrical rocket could deliver 60% of its total weight as payload.

The great advantage of the efficient electrical rockets is their ability to carry more payload. While chemical rockets may continue to be the high-speed "passenger liners" that carry people and high-priority cargo to the Moon, Mars and Venus, electrical rockets will be the "freighters" that haul the heavy supplies.

For missions to Jupiter and beyond, there's very little difference in the total flight time between chemical and electrical rockets. Such missions are measured in years, either way. Since the electrical rockets will still have a clear-cut advantage in payload, there's little doubt that they'll be chosen for such long voyages.

And, strangely enough, electrical rockets have already found a use right here at home, in Earth orbit. Very small electrical *resistojet* motors have been used on several satellites to provide pinpoint control of the satellite's position in space. With microscopic puffs of thrust, the resistojets can delicately point a satellite in precisely the direction that the ground controllers desire. Also, for satellites that are in nearly synchronous orbits, resistojets can help to push the satellite back into its proper location over the Earth whenever it starts to drift too far from the desired spot. In this application, usually called *stationkeeping*, the low thrust from the electrical rocket is a positive advantage. And, of course, the electrical rocket's high efficiency means that it can be used many, many times before running out of fuel.

Three Types of Electrical Rockets

The resistojet is one of the simplest type of electrical rocket. There are three main types of electrical rocket engines: electro-thermal (which includes the resistojet), electromagnetic, and electrostatic.

The electrothermal rocket is actually little more than the plasma jet we discussed earlier in this chapter. It uses electrical energy to heat a propellant.

The resistojet is the "baby brother" of this clan of electrothermal rockets. Simple resistance heaters, like the heating elements in an electric stove, are used to heat the propellant. They are truly tiny devices; you can fit one in your hand easily, and they weigh only a few kilograms, complete with a multi-year supply of propellant.

Within this size and weight, a resistojet unit can produce a thrust of a few hundredths of a kilogram, at a cost of less than 100 watts of electrical power. The propellant is usually nitrogen or ammonia.

Larger plasma jets, like those used for materials testing in plasma-arc wind tunnels, heat the propellant with an electric arc. They have developed close to a kilogram of thrust, with specific impulses of up to 2000 seconds. The basic limitation of the plasma jet is a phenomenon called "frozen flow losses." As heat energy is added to the propellant, the molecules of the propellant move faster and faster. In the rocket nozzle, this motion is directed and utilized to create thrust.

Up to a certain point, the more heat put into the propellant, the higher the thrust. But there comes a point where the addition of more energy causes the molecules to break apart, dissociate, or to become ionized. The energy that goes into dissociation and ionization doesn't go into thrust. As far as the rocket is concerned, this energy is lost. This so-called "frozen flow loss" limits plasma jets to top temperatures of about 17,000°K; beyond that point the frozen flow losses soak up any further input of heat energy.

As we've seen before, though, there are many ways to impart energy to a plasma. Heating is the simplest. But electromagnetic energy can be used to accelerate a plasma. In an MHD generator, the plasma stream is actually slowed down slightly as electrical energy is taken out of it. It's possible to reverse this process: accelerate a plasma stream by adding electromagnetic energy. This is the principle of the *electromagnetic rockets*.

One of the most promising of the electromagnetic type of electrical rocket is called the *MPD arc*. MPD stands for *magnetoplas-*

madynamic, which means exactly the same thing as magnetohydrodynamic. But jargon is jargon, and MPD arc has become the accepted name for this kind of rocket.

In principle, the MPD arc is little more than an ordinary plasma
arc with a magnetic field coil wrapped around it.

The plasma created by the arc is sufficiently ionized so that it
will have a strong interaction with the magnetic field. The field is
shaped to do two things: (1) add further acceleration force to the
plasma stream without significantly raising its temperature; and

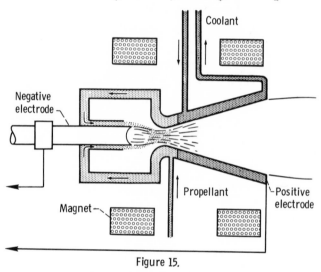

Figure 15.

MPD ARC *type of electrical rocket uses plasma arc jet plus magnetic
fields to provide increased thrust and efficiency. (National Aeronautics and Space Administration)*

(2) help keep the plasma stream away from the walls of the rocket
nozzle, to prevent heat losses and to minimize the necessity for
cooling systems to protect the nozzle.

MPD arcs deliver specific impulses of 2000 to 5000 seconds, with
thrust levels of perhaps half a kilogram. With the advent of superconducting magnets, MPD arcs might not require any more electrical power than a conventional plasma jet.

The third type of electrical rocket isn't, strictly speaking, a
plasma device. But a knowledge of plasma physics is needed to
make it work.

This is the *electrostatic rocket,* often called the *ion rocket.* As the name implies, the ion rocket accelerates a stream of ions to create thrust.

The electrostatic rocket uses electrical fields to accelerate the propellant. The particles in the propellant must be electrically charged, of course. Electrons are easily accelerated, because they're so light. But for exactly that reason they produce very little thrust in comparison to the electrical power needed to accelerate them. For the same amount of electrical power, ions can be accel-

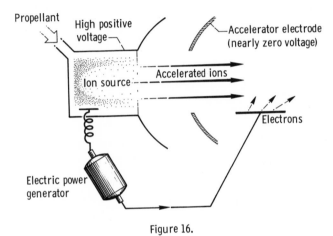

Figure 16.

ION ROCKET *uses electrostatic forces to accelerate ions to high velocity, then recombines ions with electrons to produce neutral plasma exhaust. (National Aeronautics and Space Administration)*

erated to almost the same speed, and their heavier mass produces more actual thrust.

Cesium is often used as the propellant in ion rockets, since it's easily ionized by any of several methods. Once ionized, the electrons are removed from the stream and the ions are accelerated by two forces: their mutual repulsion, and an accelerator electrode that draws them toward the exit nozzle. Immediately outside the nozzle, the electrons are ejected and rejoin the ions to form a neutral exhaust stream.

If the electrons were separated from the ions and not replaced downstream, the ions would quickly stop accelerating at the mouth of the nozzle. Their natural self-repulsion would cause a backward force, with the ions just outside the nozzle repelling the ions still in the nozzle. The resulting traffic jam would reduce the rocket's thrust to zero.

Ion rockets have shown themselves capable of specific impulses from 5000 to 100,000 seconds. But their thrusts are minuscule: ten grams or less. Still, for very deep space missions, the efficient ion "tortoise" may well be the winner against the blazing chemical rocket "hare."

Ion rockets have been tested not only in the laboratory, but in orbit. Both NASA and the Air Force have run ion rockets aboard experimental satellites. Several Russian spacecraft have carried plasma rockets, presumably similar to our MPD arcs, for testing in space. And, of course, resistojets have been used since 1964 to control the attitude of unmanned satellites and for stationkeeping.

Electrical Power Requirements

Electrical rockets need electrical power. The tiny resistojets can work on power from batteries, but larger electrical rockets will need something like 100 kilowatts per kilogram of thrust. While the instantaneous power level might be rather low for an ion rocket—say, one kilowatt—the ion rocket will need that power for many months continuously on missions deep into interplanetary space.

One way to supply electrical power is with a nuclear reactor and energy conversion device. This approach is called the *nuclear electric rocket,* as opposed to the nuclear thermal rocket, where the reactor provides heat energy rather than electricity. NASA and AEC are developing nuclear spacecraft electric power generators under a program called SNAP. But nuclear reactors, with their shielding requirements, are rather heavy for most foreseeable electrical rocket missions.

This is why both NASA's Lewis Space Research Center and Jet Propulsion Laboratory are investigating nuclear-MHD powerplants. With an MHD generator replacing the conventional turbogenerator of the SNAP system, a nuclear powerplant light enough to be useful for electrical rockets might result.

SERT II *satellite was used by NASA in 1970 for Space Electric Rocket Test of two ion rockets. The rocket thrusters were fired continuously for several months. The large "wings" on the satellite are panels of solar cells which convert sunlight into electricity, for powering the thrusters.*

Another possibility is the *solar cell*, which converts the energy of sunlight directly into electricity. For the power levels needed by electrical rockets, large panels of solar cells are needed. And as we consider flights further away from the sun, beyond Mars, these "sails" of solar panels must get bigger and bigger, since the intensity of solar energy falls off with distance.

The MPD arc seems well matched to a solar panel, however. It requires low-voltage, high-current electrical power, which is what solar cells produce. For missions as far as Mars, solar-cell-driven MPD arcs might be the best choice.

There are several other ways to generate electricity aboard a spacecraft, of course, such as fuel cells, thermionic diodes, and so on. Each of these techniques has advantages and drawbacks. But for the multi-kilowatts of power that will be needed by electrical rockets, it seems that only solar panels or nuclear generators will be equal to the task.

High Power Plasma Pockets

Electrical rockets and nuclear thermal rockets will give solid advances in performance over the chemical rockets in use today. When specific impulses are increased by factors of from two to 250, the whole picture of space exploration and economics will change radically.

But this is by no means the best that plasma technology has to offer. Electrical and nuclear thermal rockets might be compared to the improvements in aircraft engines that took place between World War I and World War II: steady, quiet, unspectacular improvement, the kind of improvement that spells the difference between an interesting bit of technology and a viable, successful industry.

But plasma technology might be able to produce something as different for rockets as the jet engine was for aircraft. By combining nuclear power with plasma engineering, rockets of truly enormous power and efficiency might be developed.

Consider nuclear energy first. Currently, nuclear reactors use only solid fission elements. The fissionable uranium, thorium, plutonium, or what-have-you is kept at a temperature low enough to remain solid. If you want to truly take advantage of the energy inherent in nuclear fission, you want to use as high a temperature as possible. This would mean turning the fissionable material into a gas and making a *gas core reactor*.

There's nothing extraordinary about this. Uranium becomes gaseous at 4091°K, and forms perfectly reasonable compounds such as uranium hexafluoride $(UF_4)$and uranium oxide (UO_2, UO_3), etc. The gas is very heavy and radioactive, but it still follows the basic gas laws that we discussed in Chapter 2.

In theory, at least, we can picture a gas core reactor in which gaseous uranium heats a propellant such as hydrogen, which is then exhausted to provide thrust. By heating the propellant with a heat source in excess of 4000°K, it's possible to attain specific impulses and exhaust velocities that are double or triple those of solid core nuclear thermal rockets. In theory.

The practical rocket engineer will point to several glaring problems with a gas core reactor. First, there's the problem of transferring the heat energy from the gaseous uranium to the propellant —without losing the uranium.

If you allow the propellant to mix directly with the uranium in the reactor core, then when you exhaust the hydrogen through the rocket nozzle, how do you prevent the uranium from going out with it? Unless you hold the uranium inside in some fashion, it will all go overboard in a matter of seconds. Several schemes have been considered, such as forcing the gases inside the core to swirl violently so that the heavier uranium compound stays in the center of the vortex and the lighter hydrogen swings out to the rim, where ducts carry it away.

Although several such concepts for containing the uranium have been investigated, none of them appears to be close to practical reality. For that reason, some engineers have suggested that the propellant shouldn't be admitted to the reactor core. Instead, it should be heated in a *heat exchanger*.

A heat exchanger is a device for doing just what its name says. It transfers heat from a hot source to a cooler substance. In the case of the gas-core-reactor rocket, the heat exchanger would transfer heat from the gaseous uranium to the propellant. The uranium stays in a closed loop, going from the reactor core to the heat exchanger and back to the core again. The propellant goes from its storage tank to the heat exchanger, where it soaks up energy and is accelerated, and then leaves the rocket nozzle. The uranium stays on board the spacecraft, and the propellant might not even become very radioactive.

But life isn't always that simple. For one thing, the uranium gas will cool slightly when it leaves the reactor core, so that it won't be at its hottest in the heat exchanger. The propellant therefore won't get as much energy as it would if it were allowed to go into the reactor core.

Another problem is in the materials used to construct the heat exchanger. While it seems possible to build a core vessel that can hold gaseous uranium at more than 4000°K, the particular problems of building heat exchangers are considerably more serious. It might well be that practical heat exchangers won't be able to handle anything near the highest temperature of the uranium. The gaseous uranium might have to be cooled down considerably before it enters the heat exchanger, thereby throwing away a good part of the advantage of going to a gas core system.

The basic problem, then, is that the gas core reactor has more energy inherent in it than can usefully be transferred to the propellant. What's needed is some better way of transferring energy. To Richard Rosa, this situation is made to order for an MHD generator.

As you recall from Chapter 5, the MHD generator is an energy conversion device, turning the thermal energy of a plasma into electricity. And the MHD generator loves high temperatures!

Rosa pictures a gas core rocket system where an MHD generator stands between the reactor core and the solid-walled heat exchanger. The uranium gas must be ionized, either directly by thermal ionization or by addition of a small amount of seed material. The resulting plasma goes through the MHD generator, where some of its energy is extracted in the form of electricity. In the MHD generator, the uranium plasma's temperature is lowered (the price for taking out electrical energy) and when the plasma leaves the MHD channel, its temperature could be low enough for the solid-walled heat exchanger to handle it comfortably.

The hydrogen propellant enters the heat exchanger and is heated to the highest temperature that the solid walls can handle. Then the propellant goes into an electrical rocket, perhaps of the MPD arc type, where the electrical energy from the MHD generator is added to it, accelerating the propellant to a still-higher velocity.

The MPD arc in this system isn't the tiny unit that would be used in low-thrust electrical rockets. It's big enough to handle a large flow of plasma, and thus produce a high thrust. MPD arcs appear to be scalable to large sizes, as are most plasma devices.

Thus the hydrogen propellant is accelerated to a higher velocity than it would have had from the heat exchanger alone. Rosa has estimated that this nuclear-MHD rocket could yield a specific impulse and exhaust velocity that's almost equal to that which would be obtained if the propellant were mixed directly with the gaseous uranium in the reactor core.

Such a gas core nuclear-MHD rocket could be the key to true interplanetary travel. This type of rocket could provide both the tons of thrust needed for boosting large spacecraft off the ground, and the high efficiency necessary for deep-space voyages with heavy payloads.

When expeditionary teams head out for the moons of Jupiter or Saturn, when large numbers of people want to fly to Mars in a few weeks rather than many months, when men want to explore the farthest reaches of our solar system, they will travel in spacecraft driven by high-power plasma engines: gas core reactors with MHD energy transfer units and electrical accelerators.

To the Stars

Plasma propelled spacecraft may be able to take inquisitive men to the farthest reaches of the solar system. But there's such an enormous gulf between our family of planets and the stars that most scientists flatly claim that interstellar flight is impossible.

The distances are staggering. Where the planets are millions of kilometers away, the stars are millions of millions of kilometers distant. Light, travelling at 300,000 kilometers per second, needs 4.3 years to go from our sun to Alpha Centauri, the nearest star.

If we improved the performance of the SATURN V booster, so that its final burnout velocity was 16 kilometers per second instead of the 11.2 km/sec it now produces, the rocket could leave the solar system and head for the stars. At that burnout velocity, coasting the rest of the way to Alpha Centauri, it would need about a million years to reach its destination.

Clearly, interstellar flight is going to need a type of engine far more powerful and efficient than anything we've seen so far. Even so, there appears to be a fundamental speed limit in the universe: the speed of light. According to modern physical theory, nothing in the universe can exceed this speed. So no matter how powerful our starship's engines, it will still need at least 4.3 years to reach the nearest star, and 100,000 years to cross the Milky Way galaxy.

Now that we've sketched the dark side of the problem, let's look at some of the brighter possibilities for answers.

First, it's possible to consider going to the stars on voyages that take eons of time. The ship, coasting slowly through interstellar space, would be a sort of stellar ark, with generations of people being born and dying on board. The distant descendants of the original wayfaring families would eventually reach the destination star.

If you want to see Alpha Centauri personally, though, there are two other possibilities. One is *cryogenic sleep,* where the astronaut is quick-frozen under high pressure so that his body can be preserved indefinitely. The astronaut can thus sleep away the millenia and be awakened by automatic equipment when he arrives at his destination. Of course, no one has been successfully frozen and re-awakened yet (no one's even volunteered to try!) and any reasonable engineer would blanch at the thought of building self-regulating equipment that would function perfectly for century after century. But in concept, it's a possibility.

The second possibility is for fast, direct flight to the stars. It takes advantage of a curious effect that comes with speeds near the velocity of light. According to Einstein and most physicists, time contracts when you travel close to the speed of light.

The physicists insist that you can't go faster than light, and you probably can't even reach the speed of light itself. But there's no reason why a spacecraft couldn't reach 99 percent of that speed, given powerful-enough engines. At nearly the speed of light, time begins to change, to slow down. A few heartbeats aboard the ship might take centuries of Earth time. Aboard the ship, everything would seem quite normal. But to an observer on Earth, time would be stretched out on the ship. This *time dilation* effect means that a ship could cross the Milky Way in a few years of ship's time. But when the ship returns to Earth, after a 10-year-long voyage, Earth will be 200,000 years older! Time will have passed at a different rate for the ship's crew.

As far as basic physics is concerned, then, interstellar flight is within the limits of possibility. Whether or not it's desirable is another matter.

But for interstellar flight to be physically possible, we must have engines of undreamed-of-power, far beyond the capabilities of even gas-core-reactor rockets. There is, even today, the hope of such an engine. The power of thermonuclear fusion, the same fusion energy that makes the stars shine, might be harnessed for an interstellar rocket engine. The power of the stars themselves might drive men out to the stars.

Many scientists and engineers all over the world are working hard to build a controlled thermonuclear reactor. Their motivation is not rocketry, but power for Earth's ever-growing masses of people. We'll look at their work in the next chapter. For now, we should consider three aspects of thermonuclear power for space flight.

First: Some scientists, such as Freeman J. Dyson of the Institute for Advanced Studies at Princeton, have advocated a spacecraft that's propelled by the explosive power of hydrogen bombs. Starting from an orbit around the Earth, such a spacecraft would be pushed along by the bomb explosions, and could achieve a velocity of one-third the speed of light within ten days. A considerable amount of theoretical work was done on this idea under the name of *Project Orion.*

There seems to be no reason why such a spacecraft couldn't be made to work efficiently and safely—except for the legal fact that nuclear explosions in space are now outlawed by international treaty. The *Orion* concept at least has the simplicity of using thermonuclear energy in the only way we presently know how to use it: in hydrogen bombs.

Second: Dwain F. Spencer and Leonard D. Jaffe, of NASA's Jet Propulsion Laboratory, pointed out in 1962 that a fusion-powered rocket could make flights to the stars in reasonable times.

They showed that a five-stage fusion rocket could make a round-trip voyage to Alpha Centauri in something like 30 years. The fusion engines that they based their calculations on were theoretical projections made by nuclear scientists and engineers working on thermonuclear reactors. They assumed that the ship would accelerate to maximum velocity for a few months and then coast the rest of the way to Alpha Centauri.

And finally: A basic drawback of the rocket engine, even the fusion rocket, is that you must carry all the propellant aboard the spacecraft. While we're accustomed to aircraft and ships that carry all the fuel they need to span an ocean, and we're willing to live with spacecraft that carry enough propellant to reach the Moon or planets and return, when it comes to interstellar flight the vast distances make the propellant load almost unbearable.

The physicist Robert W. Bussard, of TRW Corporation, suggested nearly a decade ago that the ideal interstellar engine would not be a rocket, but a ramjet.

We've seen that only a hydrogen fusion engine can provide the power needed for interstellar flight. Bussard has pointed out that there's no need to carry all the fusion rocket's propellant aboard the spacecraft. Interstellar space is filled with hydrogen.

"Filled" might be the wrong word. The interstellar hydrogen is mostly in the form of a very thin gas—less than ten atoms per cubic centimeter. In some places, the hydrogen clouds are denser and they're ionized to form a plasma.

Bussard envisions a ramjet ship, with a huge scoop perhaps 1500 kilometers across, sucking in the hydrogen fuel for the fusion engine. The scoop would have to be that large to gather in enough fuel for the engine. But it needn't be a solid scoop. It could be a vast magnetic field, based perhaps on long strands of superconducting material. The hydrogen gas atoms might be ionized by high-intensity laser "headlamps" that probe ahead of the spacecraft. Atoms can be excited and ionized by laser radiation. The resulting plasma can be scooped in by the ship's magnetic funnel.

All of these ideas for interstellar ships are nothing more than ideas. And nothing less.

It's interesting to see that even in our primitive stage of space exploration, some men can already visualize reaching the stars.

While man's eventual flights to Alpha Centauri and beyond will probably use something completely different from Bussard's ram-jet or Spencer's and Jaffe's five-stage rocket, one thing seems clear: star flight will need fusion power. And long before men head star-ward, the people of this planet will need fusion power. In a sense, thermonuclear fusion is the ultimate gift of plasma physics to mankind. The next chapter will show how close we are to unwrapping that gift.

SEVEN

Plasmas for Fusion

When Bethe and Von Weizsacker discovered the source of the sun's unfailing energy, it was a moment for mankind almost exactly like *Homo erectus'* discovery of fire. For the nuclear fusion processes that power the stars can provide man with all the energy he will ever need—if nuclear fusion can be tamed and harnessed, as fire was.

The process of combining—or fusing—light elements to make heavier elements and to liberate energy is usually called *thermonuclear fusion*. The ultimate goal of plasma technology is to produce a controlled thermonuclear reactor, often referred to simply as a CTR.

What a fantastic source of energy this thermonuclear fusion process is! It's based on the relationship that Einstein uncovered, $E = mc^2$. That is, the energy that can be obtained from a given amount of matter is equal to the mass of the matter multiplied by the speed of light, squared.

When one gram of hydrogen is converted into helium, as happens in the sun, 0.7 percent of the hydrogen (0.007 gram) disappears and turns into energy. Every second the sun loses some four million tons of matter, converted into energy. This has been going on for about five billion years, and will continue for another ten billion years or so. And when the sun has converted all its hydrogen into helium it will be only 0.7 percent lighter than it is now. That relatively tiny amount of matter keeps a star shining for 15 billion years!

Using Einstein's formula, we can calculate the amount of energy liberated from the fusion of one gram of hydrogen. The actual amount of mass that's turned into energy is 0.007 gram, and the speed of light is 3×10^{10} centimeters per second.

$$E = mc^2$$
$$E = 0.007 \text{ gram} \times (3 \times 10^{10} \text{ cm/sec})^2$$
$$E = 6.3 \times 10^{18} \text{ ergs}$$

One gram of hydrogen, converted into helium, yields 6.3×10^{18} ergs. That's equal to the explosive force of 150 tons of TNT. It's equal to 160,000 kilowatt-hours of electrical power. From a single gram of hydrogen!

In 1970, the total capacity of all the electrical power generation plants in the United States was slightly more than a trillion (10^{12}) kilowatt-hours. According to most estimates, by the year 2000 the United States will be producing about ten trillion (10^{13}) kilowatt-hours of electrical power per year. All this power could be supplied by 50 tons of hydrogen. A single C-5 transport plane could airlift enough hydrogen to provide all the fuel for all the power stations in the United States for an entire year.

The United States produces roughly one-third of the whole world's output of electrical power. So 150 tons of hydrogen could supply the whole world's needs for electrical power for a year. The smallest tugboat in the Navy could carry enough hydrogen fuel to run all the world's electrical power stations for several years!

If we had controlled thermonuclear fusion.

Offspring of War

While controlled thermonuclear fusion offers to bring enormous benefits to all mankind, much of the research on CTR's actually stems from World War II and the "Cold War" that followed.

Bethe and Von Weizsacker showed that the sun and stars are

fusion reactors in 1938. Hitler's armies had already marched into Czechoslovakia and were preparing for their assault on Poland. Japan and China were at war. In September 1939 World War II began. A little more than two years later, the United States was forcibly brought into the war by attacks on Pearl Harbor and other Pacific installations.

Most research was ended by the war. Scientists on both sides were pressed into service to produce new weapons, new ideas for military use. Ballistic missiles were developed in Germany; jet engines were developed in several nations; radar, rockets, plastics, new explosives—these and many other developments were fostered by the war.

And in the United States, thanks to a letter from Einstein to President Franklin Roosevelt, scientists from many nations started work on a program to produce a nuclear fission bomb. The program was code-named the Manhattan District Project.

The bombs that ended World War II were *fission* bombs. Their energy came from the rupture of heavy atoms of uranium or plutonium, which broke down into lighter atoms and released energy in the process. Today's nuclear electrical generating stations and nuclear ships are based on the same fission principle.

When World War II ended, instead of true peace the world found itself gripped in a Cold War of tensions and arms races. Both the United States and Soviet Russia set out to build still-stronger bombs, based on the nuclear fusion principle. Scientists on both sides of the so-called Iron Curtain had grave doubts about the wisdom, the morality, even the sanity of building hydrogen bombs. But the doubters were silenced and the bombs were built. Bombs of about 50 megatons (equal to the explosive force of 50 million tons of TNT) have been tested in the atmosphere, spreading radioactive fallout all over the world.

That's the grim side of thermonuclear fusion research: its application to warfare. Hydrogen bombs are the basic weapons of a modern nation's arsenal. By the end of this century, unless significant control steps are taken, more than a dozen nations will have enough hydrogen bombs to kill everyone on Earth. Many times over.

But that frightful picture is only one side of the story. Like all technology, thermonuclear fusion work can be applied to man's benefit as well as to his destruction. Many men, especially the scientists who understand the frightfulness of our nuclear arsenals, have worked long and hard to devote their knowledge to peaceful uses. The efforts of these men, from both sides of the Iron Curtain, began to reach some measure of success as early as 1958. In that year, at the Second United Nations International Conference on the Peaceful Uses of Atomic Energy, all work on CTR's was brought out into the open. For the first time in 20 years, research that had been kept secret for military/political reasons was "declassified" and could be discussed openly. Since then, Americans, Russians, Britons and scientists and engineers of all nations have worked together to reach the goal of a successful CTR.

In a sense, they're engaged in a race. If they can achieve success before some crisis or accident touches off the bombs, they may well put an end to most of the major causes of war.

The Thermonuclear Fusion Process

Everybody knows how to make a controlled thermonuclear reactor. You bring together some 10^{27} tons of hydrogen and let nature take its course. That's how the sun and stars do it.

At the sun's core, the plasma is completely ionized and has a temperature of about 20 million degrees Kelvin. With the weight of more than 10^{27} tons of matter pressing down on the core, the plasma density there is calculated to be about 355 times the density of water; the density of our very solid planet is only 5.5 times that of water. At the sun's core, the plasma pressure must be something like 450 *billion* atmospheres. One atmosphere is the average pressure of Earth's air at sea level, slightly more than one kilogram per square centimeter; there's more than a ton of air pressure pushing on your body right now.

Under 450 billion atmospheres and a temperature of 20 million degrees, the hydrogen ions undergo fusion. But even under these conditions, fusion doesn't occur easily.

To achieve fusion, two hydrogen ions (protons) must join together. This is something that they really don't want to do. After all, they both have positive electrical charges, which repel. The closer they get, the stronger the repulsive force. This repulsive force is often called the *Coulomb barrier,* after Charles Coulomb (see Chapter 2).

To penetrate the Coulomb barrier, a particle needs enough kinetic energy—the energy of motion—to overcome this repulsive force. In other words, if the particle is going fast enough, it can crash the barrier.

Under the fantastic pressure and temperature conditions at the sun's core, the Coulomb barrier gets crashed regularly. Four hydrogen ions produce a single helium ion and liberate energy in the process. This happens either by way of the proton-proton reaction, or the more roundabout carbon chain, as we saw in Chapter 3.

In laboratories on Earth the problem is quite a bit tougher. Physicists must be satisfied with a good deal less than 10^{27} tons of working material. In fact, they deal with grams of material, not tons. This means two things:

First, they can't duplicate the temperature and pressure conditions of the sun's core. They must find a different combination of temperature and pressure that will allow fusion reactions to take place. As we'll soon see, they usually go to even higher temperatures than the sun's, so that they can get away with much lower pressures.

Secondly, the physicists can't use either the proton-proton reaction or the carbon chain. Under the conditions attainable in the laboratory, both these reactions go much too slowly. The most optimistic scientists in the world don't dare to hope to achieve fusion conditions for more than a few seconds at a time in man-made apparatus. Inside the sun, where there's so much material available, even rather leisurely reactions are perfectly good enough to produce sustained, continuous fusion. On Earth, a faster fusion reaction is needed, because there's no way to hold a plasma at fusion conditions for more than a few seconds.

Hydrogen One, Two, and Three

Before going any further, we need to know what an *isotope* is. Just as automobiles come in many body styles, elements come in many isotopes. There are three isotopes of hydrogen. Almost all the hydrogen in the world—in the universe—is made of atoms that have one proton for a nucleus and a single electron orbiting around it. But there are other possibilities. If you add a neutron to the nucleus, the resulting atom is still hydrogen. It still has only one orbiting electron, which is what determines its chemical behavior. But although it's still the element hydrogen, this new atom is twice as heavy as "regular" hydrogen. Such atoms exist in nature and even have a name of their own: *deuterium.* Deuterium is an isotope of hydrogen.

There's also *tritium,* a still-heavier isotope that has two neutrons in its nucleus. But it's still hydrogen. Strictly speaking, "ordinary" hydrogen is also an isotope, and is sometimes called *protium.* Water made with deuterium or tritium is called *heavy water,* for obvious reasons.

Hydrogen, then, comes in three isotopes:

Element Symbol & Atomic Mass	Isotope Name	Particles in Nucleus	Relative Abundance
H^1	Protium	One proton	5000
H^2	Deuterium	One proton, one neutron	1
H^3	Tritium	One proton, two neutrons	trace

The "relative abundance" column shows that for every 5000 atoms of protium on Earth there's one deuterium atom. Tritium is very rare, and only traces of it have been found in nature. It's been produced in laboratories, for the most part.

When you find an atomic nucleus that has two protons, you no longer have hydrogen at all; you have helium. The most common isotope of helium has two neutron in the nucleus with the two protons; its atomic mass symbol is He^4. There's also the isotope He^3, with only one neutron. Many elements exist in nature in a variety of isotopes.

The reason for talking about isotopes is that the controlled thermonuclear reactor experiments all make use of deuterium and tritium. Instead of using protium, as the sun does, physicists have turned to these heavier isotopes of hydrogen because their fusion reaction rates are fast enough to allow some chance of producing fusion in a man-made apparatus, with its fleeting moment of containment time.

Deuterium Fusion

The deuterium reaction works this way:

Two deuterons (deuterium nuclei) can interact with each other in two equally-likely ways. Either they'll combine to form a triton (tritium nucleus) and a free proton, or they'll form a helium-3 nucleus and a free neutron. A deuteron will react with a triton to form "ordinary" helium, He^4, and a free neutron. And a deuteron will combine with a triton to form He^4 and a free proton. Each of these reactions produces energy in the millions of electron volts.

So a deuteron plasma, under the proper conditions, will go through these reactions, forming tritium and then helium, while liberating energy. It will also liberate some high-energy neutrons, which form a serious radiation hazard that must be shielded against. More on that later.

We can write these reactions in the shorthand of physicists, with the following symbols:

D^2 = deuteron (deuterium nucleus)
T^3 = triton (tritium nucleus)
He^3 = helium-3 nucleus
He^4 = helium-4 nucleus
n^1 = neutron
H^1 = proton (protium nucleus)

The deuterium-deuterium reactions are:

1. $D^2 + D^2 \longrightarrow He^3 + n^1 + 3.2\ \text{MeV}$ ⎱ equal
2. $D^2 + D^2 \longrightarrow T^3 + H^1 + 4.0\ \text{MeV}$ ⎰ probability
3. $D^2 + T^3 \longrightarrow He^4 + n^1 + 17.6\ \text{MeV}$
4. $D^2 + He^3 \longrightarrow He^4 + H^1 + 18.3\ \text{MeV}$

As you can see, the deuterium–deuterium reactions (usually written D–D reactions) don't produce as much energy as the D–T and D–He^3 combinations. Physicists would prefer, therefore, to build their CTR's around the D–T reaction.

To picture how these reactions take place, imagine a tankful of deuterium gas, sitting in its container at room temperature and one atmosphere of pressure. The average kinetic energy of the deuterium molecules is 0.04 electron volt. One eV represents the energy of motion of a particle that corresponds to a temperature of 11,640°K. At 0.04 eV, the deuterium molecules are lazing along at a mere 4800 kilometers per hour, slightly better than the speed of a supersonic transport plane.

Now we heat the gas to 5000°K. The molecules dissociate, break up, and we have a gas composed of deuterium atoms. The pressure rises to 40 atmospheres, and the average speed of the deuterium atoms reaches some 64,000 km/hr. If we push the temperature to 100,000°K, the atoms become ionized and we get a plasma consisting of free electrons and bare deuterium nuclei, deuterons. The pressure is now 1500 atmospheres. The average velocity of the plasma's electrons is 16 million km/hr; the heavier deuterons are plodding along at "only" 270,000 km/hr.

The walls of any solid container would have long ago been vaporized by any sustained contact with such a ferociously hot, high-pressure plasma. Yet even at these conditions, fusion can't take place.

The problem is the Coulomb barrier. Each deuteron has a positive electrical charge, and it takes an energy of about 100 keV to overcome the electrostatic barrier between two deuterons. We must pump more energy into the deuterons.

At one million degrees Kelvin, fusion reactions start to occur often enough to be measurable. But the energy output from these reactions is pitifully small, only a few millionths of a watt per cubic centimeter of plasma. Deuterons are fusing, all right, but most of the fusion energy is coming out in ways that aren't useful to us, and thus the energy is lost. At 100 million degrees, the plasma pressure goes up to 1.5 million atmospheres, the deuterons are roaring along at 2400 kilometers *per second,* and fusion energy is streaming from the plasma at a rate of 100,000 kilowatts per cubic centimeter.

Our deuterium plasma is now rivalling the conditions at the sun's core. Although the pressure is far lower than the sun's central pressure, our plasma's temperature is five times higher than the sun's. And it's producing fusion energy.

But even now we don't have the proper conditions for a controlled thermonuclear reactor. Because at 100 million degrees, we must still put more energy into the plasma than the plasma will give us back from fusion reactions.

It's only when we get the plasma to about 350 million degrees that the fusion reactions will produce enough energy to become self-sustaining. At that temperature—called the *ignition temperature*—the deuterons will yield continuous power output without any further input of energy. As long as fresh deuterium is fed into this star-hot furnace, power will be produced continuously.

The Fusion Experiments

We know now what's needed, in theory, to produce a sustained thermonuclear fusion reaction. Scientists and engineers have translated these theoretical needs into practical requirements for a fusion reactor. Assuming that the reactor's fuel will be either pure deuterium or a mixture of deuterium and tritium, there are three requirements for sustained fusion:

1. The ion temperature must be between 100 million and one billion degrees Kelvin, corresponding to 10^4 to 10^5 eV.
2. The density of the plasma must be about 10^{15} ions per cubic centimeter (roughly 10^{-4} of the density of sea-level air).
3. The ions must be kept at this temperature and density for at least a few hundredths of a second; this is called *confinement*.

There's some give-and-take in these requirements. If the plasma density is higher than 10^{15} ions/cm^3, then the confinement time can be shorter. If the plasma becomes very much denser, the confinement time can be extremely short. But the energy release will be violent; we'd have a bomb, not a controlled reactor.

For that reason, plasma densities are kept low, even though this makes confinement an excruciatingly difficult task.

In fact, the key to controlled fusion is this task of plasma confinement—holding the deuterium plasma at the necessary temperature and density long enough to get a sustained fusion reaction going. A tenth of a second is only an eyeblink in our human frame of reference, but inside a star-hot plasma it's time enough for the deuterons to race back and forth across the length of the plasma a million times or more. *Something* must hold them, contain them, turn them around when they reach the surface of the plasma. Otherwise the deuterium plasma will simply evaporate, like a puff of smoke.

Whatever it is that confines the plasma, it can't be a solid, material wall. But not for the reason that first comes to mind. At a temperature of 100 million degrees, no solid material could stand up to the hot plasma without being instantly vaporized. True enough—but only if the plasma is dense enough to actually contain a large amount of heat. That isn't the case in fusion experiments.

Remember, the deuterium plasma is at a density that's ten thousand times lower than atmospheric. So even though its temperature is astronomical, its real heat content—in typical fusion experiments—is minuscule. A liter of deuterium plasma at this density and a temperature of 350 million degrees has a heat content of only 18,000 calories. That's just about enough to warm a cup of coffee!

The reason that the plasma mustn't touch the solid walls of its container is that such contact will immediately cool the plasma and end the fusion experiment. If fusion temperature is to be maintained, then the plasma must be kept off the walls.

How do you hold a star-hot plasma in the middle of a vacuum tank without letting it touch the solid walls? With a *magnetic bottle,* of course. Magnetic fields can not only contain and confine the plasma, they can even help to heat it to the fusion ignition temperature.

In theory, at least.

The first attempts at producing fusion in a magnetic bottle depended on what's called the *pinch effect.* The basic idea was to drive a strong electrical current through the plasma, and let the magnetic field induced by the current do the twin jobs of confining and heating the plasma.

In pinch experiments, the deuterium gas was placed in an insulated tube. Electrical currents of millions of amps were applied to the tube. The gas immediately broke down into a plasma and

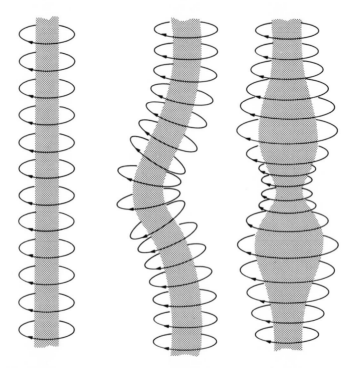

PINCHES AND KINKS. *Early fusion experiments attempted to confine and heat plasma with magnetic pinch effect (left). But instabilities caused kinks in plasma column and prevented attainment of fusion.*

the pinching magnetic field appeared. A magnetic field is always created by moving electrical charges. The effect of the field was to squeeze the plasma toward the middle of the tube. And as the plasma was confined, or pinched, its pressure grew and its temperature soared.

All this took place in a few millionths of a second. But although the pinch effect did appear and did what was theoretically predicted, it didn't last long enough to produce fusion. Within those few millionths of a second, instabilities appeared in the pinched plasma. The plasma wouldn't stay still, wouldn't remain in a steady column. Kinks and wobbles appeared in the plasma, and the hot

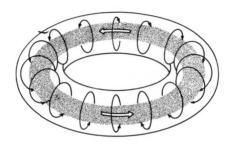

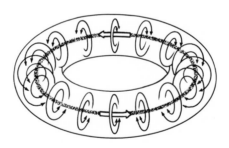

STELLERATOR *device used pinch effect in closed toroidal machine to avoid problems associated with ends of plasma column. While instabilities also defeated earliest Stellerator designs, recent Russian Tokamak machines apparently have used a similar geometry with great success.*

deuterium quickly leaked out of the magnetic field and cooled off.

The tighter and harder the pinch applied to the plasma, the faster and more violent the instabilities. It was scant consolation that plasma physicists had predicted such instabilities. Their mathematical analyses of the interactions of a magnetic field with the plasma showed that such instabilities would appear.

It soon became clear that attempts to confine and heat a deuterium plasma by generating magnetic fields within the plasma itself would always be defeated by instabilities. So fusion scientists turned to the idea of producing magnetic fields outside the plasma and using them to confine the plasma. A magnetic field of 50,000 gauss, for example, can withstand a plasma pressure of 100 atmospheres. A field of 500,000 gauss could hold a plasma at a pressure of 10,000 atmospheres. Very strong magnetic fields can be generated for a few seconds by powerful electromagnets. And superconducting magnets (see Chapter 5) have achieved continuous operation at fields of several hundred thousand gauss.

You recall from Chapter 4 that the electrons and ions in the Van Allen belts circulate back and forth from pole to pole around our

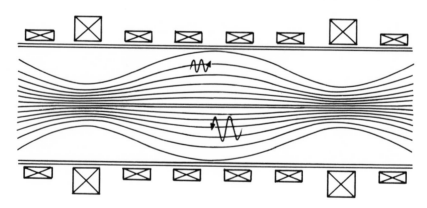

MAGNETIC MIRROR *devices use strong magnetic fields at the ends to force charged particles in the plasma to "mirror" and reverse direction, thereby remaining confined within the machine. Particles along centerline tend to escape, however. And the weaker field in the middle section gives rise to charge-interchange instabilities. Arrows denote motions of electron (top) and proton.*

Earth. As they spiral around the magnetic lines of force in the magnetosphere, they "mirror" and reverse direction near the magnetic poles, where the field lines squeeze together tightly. Fusion scientists seized on this "mirroring" idea to build a magnetic bottle for their plasma.

The *magnetic mirror* type of fusion device has magnetic field coils at each end to produce a strong field. The effect is similar to the situation in the Van Allen belts near the geomagnetic poles. Electrons and ions in the plasma approach the ends of the magnetic mirror machine and find their spiralling motions become tighter and tighter as the field lines squeeze together. At last their motion reverses, "mirrors," and they go speeding back the way they came.

But there are two problems. First, some of the plasma particles happen to be spiralling along field lines that come out at the middle of the mirror section, and these particles can pass right through and out of the device. Thus, some of the plasma leaks away. This isn't catastrophic, and in fact this leak can be turned into an advantage under certain situations. More on that later.

The second problem is very serious, though.

In the center of the magnetic-mirror device the magnetic field bulges outward. The farther away from the centerline of the device, the weaker the field is. As a particle goes spiralling along, it feels less of a force on the part of its spiral that is farthest away from the center of the machine. This makes it tend to drift outward. Worse still, the ions and electrons drift in two different directions, since they're spiralling in different directions to begin with, due to their different electrical charges.

The plasma begins to break apart. The ions are collecting on one side of the machine and the electrons on the other. An electric field is produced by this separation of the charges, and this just pushes them apart faster. Very quickly the plasma dissipates entirely out of the magnetic field. The experiment has collapsed.

This kind of instability has been called by many names, not all of them printable. Most often it's referred to as the *interchange instability* or the *flute instability*. "Interchange" refers to the separation of ions and electrons in the plasma. "Flute" has nothing to do with music. It's a description of the ruffled appearance of the plasma column, like the surface of a fluted pillar in a Greek temple. Flute-interchange instabilities defeated all the early attempts to produce fusion in a simple magnetic mirror apparatus.

The Russian physicist M. F. Ioffe showed a simple solution to the flute-interchange instabilities. The basic problem with the magnetic mirror device was that the plasma particles could leak away in the middle of the machine, in the region between the two strong magnetic mirror coils. Ioffe produced a design where there were strong magnetic fields all around the plasma. He did this simply by placing four current-carrying rods between the mirror coils. The

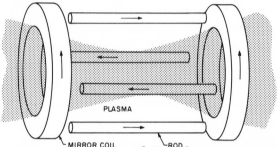

MAGNETIC WELL *geometry with Ioffe bars prevents interchange instabilities of earlier magnetic mirror machines. Current-carrying bars, or rods, confine plasma thoughout the active region of the device.*

current flowing in the rods creates a magnetic field. No matter where the plasma goes, it faces a magnetic field that gets stronger as the plasma strays farther from the center of the apparatus. This kind of configuration is now called a *magnetic well*. The current-carrying rods have become known throughout the world as *Ioffe bars*.

The magnetic well is a tremendously important step toward controlled fusion. The major instability problems, such as flute-interchange instabilities, have been licked by the magnetic well configuration. While very little fanfare has been made in public about this, history will probably show that the invention of the magnetic well idea was as important to mankind as the invention of the steam engine.

But although the major instabilities in fusion plasmas can now be controlled, there are subtler problems that still stand in the way of controlled fusion.

These micro-instabilities fall generally into the category of *wave-particle instabilities*. They stem from the sharing of energy in the plasma between the particles and the electromagnetic forces. Although wave-particle instabilities aren't as obviously destructive as the gross instabilities of the flute-interchange type, they can still lead to a complete disruption of the plasma and an end to any possibility of achieving fusion conditions. The major effort of the world's fusion scientists at present is aimed at understanding and overcoming these micro-instabilities. And once that is accomplished, controlled thermonuclear fusion will be a reality.

Fusion Machines

Over the years, fusion scientists in many nations have built a colorful variety of experimental devices in their attempts to produce controlled fusion.

The original pinch tubes gave way, at Princeton University, to a doughnut-shaped apparatus called the *Stellerator*. This was actually a pinch tube that was circular and closed on itself, so that there were no ends for the plasma to leak out of. One of the earliest fusion experiments, at Los Alamos Scientific Laboratory, involved an experimental rig that was smilingly called the *Perhapsatron*. The University of California Radiation Laboratory at Livermore produced an *Astron*. And in the 1960's, as magnetic mirror and magnetic well devices became popular, names such as *Octupole*, *Scylla*, *2X*, and *Phoenix* were given to various pieces of experimental hardware by hopeful physicists and engineers.

At Livermore, a "baseball coil" machine has been built where the magnetic field coil is shaped somewhat like the stitched seam on a baseball. It's also sometimes called the "tennis ball" machine, reflecting a difference of sporting preferences among the workers there.

But of all the devices built to date, the most exciting is the Russian *Tokomak T-3*. Not much is known outside Russia about the details of the Tokomak T-3 configuration. But its performance is known, and has been verified by a team of British researchers who were invited to work with their Russian colleagues. The Tokomak T-3 has come tremblingly close to producing a sustained fusion reaction. Listed below are the conditions for sustained fusion that we cited earlier in this chapter, together with the performances of several fusion devices.

			CONDITIONS ACHIEVED BY:		
	Tokomak	*LRL**	*GGA*	*LASL*	*England*
Required condition	*T-3*	*2X*	*Octupole*	*Scylla*	*Phoenix II*
Ion temperature of 10^8–10^9 degrees K	10^6	10^7	10^5	10^7	10^8
Plasma density of 10^{15} ions/cm^3	10^{13}	10^{13}	10^{10}	10^{16}	10^9
Confinement time of at least 10^{-2} second	10^{-2}	10^{-4}	10^{-2}	10^{-5}	10^{-1}

*LRL = Lawrence Radiation Laboratory; GGA = Gulf General Atomic; LASL = Los Alamos Scientific Laboratory

As the table shows, the Tokomak T-3 has achieved the most promising combination of temperature, density and confinement time. The 2X, Scylla, and Phoenix II have all produced higher plasma temperatures. Phoenix II has confined its plasma for a tenth of a second, while Tokomak and the Octupole have confinement times of a few hundredths of a second, and the 2X and Scylla are much worse.

In the words of Dr. Glenn T. Seaborg, Chairman of the United States Atomic Energy Commission, "The Russian Tokomak T-3 device has the best overall performance—so good that the United States program is being revised radically to take advantage of the successes of the Russian work."

The New Possibilities

Although it's been a long time since fusion research began in earnest, the past 25 years have been solid progress toward what can only be described as the most difficult technical task man has ever set for himself. Thanks to the open-handed cooperation of scientists around the world, despite political difficulties, mankind is on the verge of producing conditions rivalling those in the cores of stars, right here on Earth.

"On the verge" may be an overly dramatic phrase. It might take another 25 years before sustained fusion is achieved in the laboratory. Or longer. But the progress to date, especially recently, has been encouraging. And the work goes on.

There are two new pieces of technology that might help to speed this work toward controlled fusion. One, we've already seen in Chapter 5: superconducting magnets. Superconductors are capable of extremely powerful magnetic field strengths—many hundreds of thousands of gauss. Fusion researchers are only beginning to take advantage of them, mainly because their experiments to date have only had time durations of fractions of a second, and therefore haven't needed the steady-state superconductors. But superconducting coils of 100, 200 thousand gauss or more, will be very helpful in confining fusion plasmas at relatively high densities.

Another shining new piece of technology that may help to produce controlled fusion is the laser.

Lasers produce beams of light, and have reached a stage of development where some fusion scientists are experimenting with them as means of heating a plasma. The light beam emitted by a laser is nothing less than a beam of energy. If a powerful laser beam is focused on a confined plasma, it can pump energy into the plasma, raise its temperature.

It would take a tremendously powerful laser to heat a deuterium plasma to its ignition temperature, but lasers have already achieved output powers high enough to make them interesting to fusion researchers. It might be that when controlled fusion is finally achieved, it will be done with a high-power laser to trigger the plasma.

Another new possibility is the concept of a *pulsed fusion reactor*.

All the fusion experiments we've spoken of so far are aimed at producing a continuous fusion reaction—even if the experiment lasts only a fraction of a second. And as we've seen, it's necessary to contain the deuterium plasma with strong magnetic fields if fusion is to take place and be sustained.

An alternate approach is to try a pulsed fusion device. Simply put, the idea is to suddenly heat a pellet of solid deuterium (or a volume of gaseous deuterium) to fusion temperature by using an outside energy source, such as a superpowerful laser. The deuterium "flashes" into a fusion plasma, releasing the desired energy. Then the plasma is carried out of the device, and a new pellet of deuterium is brought in for a new burst of power.

This "gatling gun" approach gets around the basic problem of containing a thermonuclear plasma with magnetic fields. In its simplest concept, the pulsed fusion reactor wouldn't need magnetic containment at all. The power comes out in a quick burst and the "spent" plasma is allowed to leave the device while new deuterium is brought in.

The pulsed fusion reactor is a very new idea, and may prove to be impractical. But its basic simplicity has attracted some of the best researchers in the field. Perhaps the first practical CTR's will give us a putt-putt-putt series of energy bursts rather than a continuous hum of power.

A CTR Power Station

In a sense, we've only told half the story of fusion power. For once the physicists have achieved controlled thermonuclear fusion, the engineers will have the problem of determining how to *use* the energy produced by fusion in a practical way.

The CTR will be an energy source of unparalleled magnitude, working with a fuel supply that's virtually unlimited: deuterium from the oceans. What's needed to make the CTR useful is an *energy conversion* device that will translate the fusion plasma's energy into a form that we can use. As we saw in Chapter 5, turbo-generators and MHD generators are energy conversion devices that convert the heat of fossil fuels or nuclear fission into electricity. We need something similar to go with the CTR.

One obvious suggestion is to use the enormous heat energy of the fusion plasma to run turbines and generate electricity in a more-or-less standard manner. Since the plasma's so hot, it would probably be used first to vaporize a metal such as potassium. The potassium vapor would turn a set of turbines and then—still quite hot—would be used to boil water. The resulting fusion-potassium-steam power system might have a 60% efficiency.

D-T FUSION POWER PLANT

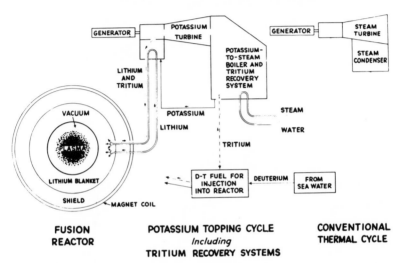

FUSION POWER PLANT *might use enormous heat of fusion reactions to run potassium turbines and generate electricity. (Atomic Energy Commission)*

Another possibility is to let some of the highly-energetic particles of the plasma leak out of confinement into an electrical grid that would collect the particles and convert their energy of motion directly into electricity. This scheme is somewhat reminiscent of the MHD generator, and might provide higher efficiency than the turbine system. There are other, more exotic, possibilities as well, including interactions between the plasma and the containment magnetic fields that would generate electricity directly.

To date, relatively little work has been done on any of these fusion-energy conversion concepts. But as the moment when sustained fusion is achieved draws closer, more and more attention will be paid to the energy conversion problem.

No matter what energy conversion system is eventually used, we can already draw an outline of what a CTR power station might look like.

The fusion process itself will no doubt take place in a magnetic well configuration. The fusion chamber will be housed inside a thick blanket of radiation shielding material—probably lead and concrete. This is because the D–D and D–T reactions produce a large number of neutrons, which are an extreme radiation danger. But the neutrons can easily be stopped by a simple radiation shield.

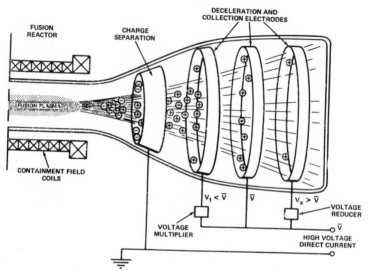

DIRECT CONVERSION FUSION PLANT *would use energetic protons and electrons from fusion plasma to generate electricity directly, in process akin to MHD power generation. (Atomic Energy Commission)*

What's more, they can be turned to useful purpose.

The neutrons carry a considerable amount of energy. If the fusion chamber is surrounded by a "jacket" containing the element lithium (Li, the third lightest element, after hydrogen and helium, and the lightest metal), the neutrons will react with the lithium atoms to produce tritium, which is part of the fuel that the reactor wants. In fact, calculations have shown that more tritium can be produced than is needed by the reactor. So the fusion reactor can "breed" extra tritium for other purposes.

And while the inner fusion chamber will be radioactive, the by-products of the fusion processes—new tritium and helium—will not be radioactive. There will be no problem of radioactive wastes to dispose of, as there is in the fission reactors now being used.

Since there'll be a very small amount of deuterium and/or tritium in the reactor at any given moment, there's no danger of a runaway reaction that could lead to an explosion. This means that CTR power stations can be located anywhere, even in the middle of thickly populated cities. And, of course, there's no air pollution because there's no combustion going on; there's no water pollution (unless steam turbines are used); and there's no radioactive pollution to worry about.

If all the predictions of the physicists are correct, CTR power stations will be quiet, clean and safe. They'll produce power at 60% efficiency or better, from fuel that's very cheap.

And more than that—CTR's may completely solve the problems of pollution and waste disposal.

The Fusion Torch

Two scientists at the Atomic Energy Commission, Dr. Bernard J. Eastlund and Dr. William C. Gough, conceived the idea of the fusion torch in the late 1960's. Very simply, they realized that the star-hot plasma of a CTR can be used to vaporize any material so completely that it's broken down into simple atoms of gas. A junk auto, for example, would be turned into a cloud of iron atoms, aluminum atoms, carbon atoms, and so forth. Standard gas separation techniques and collection equipment could collect these elements *in their pure state*. The elements could then be recycled to produce new materials or products.

Recognize that Eastlund and Gough aren't suggesting that the fusion plasma be turned directly onto the objects to be vaporized. As we've seen earlier, the plasma's too diffuse for that. It would immediately cool off, rather than heat up the solid object. But in a working CTR, where the plasma is always at fusion temperature, some of that enormous energy can be utilized as heat to vaporize waste material. Anything from garbage to battleships could be completely vaporized, returned to pure elements, and then collected as raw material.

The fusion torch, then, would not only take care of waste disposal, it would be a new source of raw material, material that's recycled from yesterday's garbage and junk. There'd be a dramatic decrease in the need for new mining, forestry, oil drilling, and other resource-gutting activities that are now devastating our planet. We'd be able to recycle our materials thoroughly, over and over again. The only new natural resources our society would need would be to replenish what's irreparably lost or to add to the existing stock of materials.

Moreover, the energy of the fusion torch can be used for many chemical and industrial processes, as well. Clean heat from fusion can aid any number of industrial processes, such as metal smelting, plastics manufacture, chemical reactions, etc.

And still more. When material is vaporized by the fusion torch, a huge amount of ultraviolet energy will be produced as a by-product. Ultraviolet energy can be used to de-salt water, to heat buildings, to kill bacteria, to enhance the growth of edible algae, and many other purposes.

The hot breath of fusion, it seems, can not only provide us with all the power we need. It can help to cleanse our world of pollution and wastes, recycle our materials, and provide ultraviolet energy for many other purposes.

The World of Fusion Power

Imagine a world where there's more than enough electrical power for every human being on Earth. Where electrical power is so cheap that sea water can be desalted and pumped inland thousands of miles to turn arid wastelands into productive food-growing territories.

Imagine a world without pollution, without the need for gutting the planet's natural resources for constantly-more metals and fuels that end up as rusting junk or cough-producing smog. Imagine a world where power is so cheap and plentiful that men can live anywhere—at the poles, under the sea, in the desert—and still ride to any place on the planet in quiet comfort within a matter of hours.

Imagine a world without war. For the basic causes of war have always been linked to lack of food, lack of natural resources, lack of wealth. Fusion power will help to grow food, recycle our resources, and make us wealthy beyond imagining.

Today, the world's governments spend a grand total of about $150 million a year on fusion research. This is about equal to the purchase price of a dozen jet fighter planes. In the United States, billions of dollars are spent each year on cigarettes and alcohol. We spend more money on bubble gum than on fusion research.

Of all the world's efforts toward fusion, the work being done in Russia is the best funded, and is clearly achieving the best results. There's no "fusion race" among the nations, as there once was a "space race." And a good thing, too. Fusion is much too important to be left to the politicians, just as war is too important to be left to the generals.

Perhaps by the end of this century, a working CTR power station will exist somewhere in the world. Long before that, MHD generators can be producing power for many cities. And plasma rockets will be propelling men toward Mars and perhaps even Jupiter, giant of the planets. Already, today, plasma physicists are working with astronomers to help learn more of how the universe works, how the sun behaves, how the plasmas in space affect our planet.

We've come a long way from *Homo erectus* and that fortunate lightning bolt. The quiet investigations of Crookes and Thomson have evolved into the world-wide quest for fusion power. The work of plasma scientists and engineers has an effect on the employment and dignity of coal miners as well as astronauts.

The years to come will see the young science of plasma physics turn into a vigorous technology, a technology that can change our world enormously—and for the better. Yet still, hidden in underground silos around the world, hydrogen bombs sit atop their missiles, waiting only the touch of a button to destroy the world as we know it. This too is a product of plasma science and technology.

Which world will we have?

Appendix I: Numbers

The Metric System

Scientists all over the world use the metric system in preference to the older and clumsier British system of inches, pounds, and so forth. In fact, even in Britain the metric system is now the official standard. Only in an increasingly small minority of countries, including the United States, are students still required to learn how many feet are in a mile, and how many ounces in a pound.

1 millimeter (mm) = 0.03937 inch
1 centimeter (cm) = 10 mm = 0.3937 inch
1 meter (m) = 100 cm = 39.37 inches, or 3.28 feet, or 1.09 yards
1 kilometer (km) = 1000 m = 0.62137 mile
1 mile = 1.6093 km
1 inch = 2.5400 cm = 25.400 mm

1 gram (gm) = 0.0353 ounce = 0.0022046 pound
1 kilogram (kg) = 1000 gm = 2.2046 pounds
1 metric ton = 1000 kg = 2204.6 pounds

1 liter (l) = 1.0567 liquid quarts
10 liters = 1 decaliter (dkl) = 2.64 gallons

Temperature Scales

Three temperature scales are in common use today. The Kelvin, or Absolute, scale is used most in this book. The Kelvin scale starts at absolute zero, the temperature where, theoretically, all molecular motion stops and the energy we call heat ceases to exist. There are no minus numbers in the Kelvin scale.

The Centigrade scale uses the same "sized" degrees as the Kelvin. The only difference between the two scales is that the Centigrade scale places its zero at the freezing point of fresh water. In converting from Centigrade to Kelvin, merely add 273; to go from Kelvin to Centigrade, subtract 273. The Fahrenheit scale is older and much different. To convert from Centigrade degrees to Fahrenheit, multiply by 9/5 and then add 32. To go from Fahrenheit to Centigrade, first subtract 32 and then multiply by 5/9.

	Degrees Kelvin	*Degrees Centigrade*	*Degrees Fahrenheit*
Water boils	373	100	212
Water freezes	273	0	32
Absolute zero	0	−273	−459

Powers of Ten Notation

When it comes to writing very large or very small numbers, the powers of ten notation saves much work.

$$1 = 10^0 \qquad\qquad 10 = 10^1$$
$$0.1 = 10^{-1} \qquad\qquad 100 = 10^2$$
$$0.01 = 10^{-2} \qquad\qquad 1000 = 10^3$$
$$0.000001 = 10^{-6} \qquad 1{,}000{,}000 = 10^6$$
$$0.000000001 = 10^{-9} \qquad 1{,}000{,}000{,}000 = 10^9$$

As you can see, a *plus* superscript tells you how many zeroes are to the left of the decimal place, and a *minus* superscript tells how many digits (not only zeroes) are to the right of the decimal. To write out a number such as 83 billion we get:

$$83 \times 10^9 \text{ or } 8.3 \times 10^{10}$$

Appendix II: Names

Light Years

Many people confuse the term *light year* with a measurement of time. It's a measurement of distance. Light travels at a velocity of almost exactly 3×10^{10} centimeters per second, in vacuum. There are 31.5×10^6 seconds in a year. Therefore:

$$(3 \times 10^{10} \text{ cm/sec}) \times (3.15 \times 10^7 \text{ sec}) = 9.45 \times 10^{17} \text{ cm}$$

This value is a close approximation. Using more exact numbers, the distance that light travels in a year is calculated to be 9.4605 trillion kilometers. This is a light year.

Because of the confusion over this term, and its somewhat romantic aura, astronomers usually prefer to use the slightly larger unit called the *parsec*, which is equal to 3.262 light years.

Names for Large and Small Units

In this book we use terms such as megawatts, kilovolts, etc. Prefixes that denote large and small units include:

tera $= 10^{12}$	deci $= 10^{-1}$
giga $= 10^9$	centi $= 10^{-2}$
mega $= 10^6$	milli $= 10^{-3}$
kilo $= 10^3$	micro $= 10^{-6}$
hecto $= 10^2$	nano $= 10^{-9}$
deka $= 10$	pico $= 10^{-12}$

For Further Reading

The books, reports and articles listed below go into more detail on the various aspects of plasma physics and engineering that are discussed in this book. Most of the entries listed here are written for the general reader. A few are texts that are intended for students of physics. These more difficult entries are marked with an asterisk(*).

Chapter 1: The Gift from the Sky

Carleton S. Coon, THE STORY OF MAN, Alfred A. Knopf, New York, 1955

William Howells, MANKIND IN THE MAKING, Doubleday & Co., New York, 1967 (revised edition)

Chapter 2: The Fourth State of Matter

(*)E. H. Holt and R. E. Haskell, FOUNDATIONS OF PLASMA DYNAMICS, Macmillan Co., New York, 1965

(*)Wulf B. Kunkel, editor, PLASMA PHYSICS IN THEORY AND APPLICATION, McGraw Hill Co., New York, 1966

Paul D. Thompson, GASES AND PLASMAS, J. B. Lippincott Co., Philadelphia, 1966

Chapter 3: The Birth and Death of Stars

Hannes Alfvén, WORLDS-ANTIWORLDS, ANTIMATTER IN COSMOLOGY, W. H. Freeman & Co., San Francisco, 1966

Ben Bova, IN QUEST OF QUASARS, Crowell–Collier Press, New York, 1970

Stephen P. Moran, *The Crab Nebula Mystery*, Smithsonian, Vol. 1 No. 3, June 1970

Otto Struve, THE UNIVERSE, MIT Press, Cambridge, 1962

Chapter 4: Plasmas and the Weather in Space

Kinsey A. Anderson, *Solar Particles and Cosmic Rays*, Scientific American, Vol. 202 No. 6, June 1960 (page 64)

Shun-Ichi Akasofu, *The Aurorae*, Scientific American, Vol. 213 No. 6, December 1965 (page 54)

R. Grant Athay, *The Solar Chromosphere*, Scientific American, Vol. 206 No. 2, February 1962 (page 50)

Horace W. Babcock, *The Magnetism of the Sun*, Scientific American, Vol. 202 No. 2, February 1960 (page 52)

Geoffrey Burbidge, *The Origin of Cosmic Rays*, Scientific American, Vol. 215 No. 2, August 1966 (page 32)

Laurence J. Cahill Jr., *The Magnetosphere*, Scientific American, Vol 212 No. 3, March 1965 (page 58)

H. H. Hess (chairman), *Physics of the Earth in Space*, Space Sciences Board report to the National Academy of Sciences, National Research Council, August 1968

William C. Livingston, *Magnetic Fields on the Quiet Sun*, Scientific American, Vol. 215 No. 5, November 1966 (page 54)

Brian J. O'Brien, *Radiation Belts*, Scientific American, Vol. 208 No. 5, May 1963 (page 84)

E. N. Parker, *The Solar Wind*, Scientific American, Vol. 210 No. 4, April 1964 (page 66)

Victor P. Starr, *The Circulation of the Sun's Atmosphere*, Scientific American, Vol. 218 No. 1, January 1968 (page 100)

Robert A. Young, *The Airglow*, Scientific American, Vol. 214 No. 3, March 1966 (page 102)

Chapter 5: Plasmas for Power

J. E. Kunzler and M. Tanenbaum, *Superconducting Magnets*, Scientific American, Vol. 206 No. 6, June 1962 (page 60)

Richard J. Rosa and Arthur Kantrowitz, *MHD Power*, International Science and Technology, September 1964

(*)Richard J. Rosa, MAGNETOHYDRODYNAMIC ENERGY CONVERSION, McGraw Hill Co., New York, 1968

MHD for Central Station Power Generation: A Plan for Action, report by the Panel on Magnetohydrodynamics of the Office of Science and Technology, June 1969

MHD Electrical Power Generation: The 1969 Status Report, Joint ENEA/IAEA International Liason Group on MHD Electrical Power Generation

Chapter 6: Plasmas for Space Flight

John V. Becker, *Re-entry from Space*, Scientific American, Vol. 204 No. 1, January 1961 (page 47)

Gabriel Giannini, *Electrical Propulsion in Space*, Scientific American, Vol. 204 No. 3, March 1961 (page 57)

(°)Wolfgang E. Moeckel, *Propulsion Systems for Manned Exploration of the Solar System*, Astronautics and Aeronautics, Vol. 7 No. 8, August 1969 (page 68)

Space Flight with Electrical Propulsion, NASA Lewis Research Center, Cleveland, 1969

(°)*What Future for Electric Propulsion?*, Special Section of Astronautics and Aeronautics, Vol. 6 No. 6, June 1968 (page 38)

Chapter 7: Plasmas for Fusion

Tom Alexander, *The Hot New Promise of Thermonuclear Power*, Fortune, Vol LXXXI No. 6, June 1970 (page 94)

Amasa S. Bishop, PROJECT SHERWOOD: THE U.S. PROGRAM IN CONTROLLED FUSION, Addison—Wesley Co., Reading, Mass., 1958

Amasa S. Bishop, *The Status and Outlook of the World Program in Controlled Fusion Research*, presentation to the National Research Council of the National Academy of Sciences, 11 March 1969

Francis F. Chen, *The Leakage Problem in Fusion Reactors*, Scientific American, Vol. 217 No. 1, July 1967 (page 76)

Bernard J. Eastlund and William C. Gough, *The Fusion Torch*, Atomic Energy Commission, 15 May 1969

T. K. Fowler and R. F. Post, *Progress Toward Fusion Power*, Scientific American, Vol. 215 No. 6, December 1966 (page 21)

William C. Gough and Bernard T. Eastlund, *Prospects of Fusion Power*, Scientific American, Vol. 224 No. 2, February 1971

Richard F. Post, *Fusion Power*, Scientific American, Vol. 197 No. 6, December 1957 (page 73)

Glenn T. Seaborg, *Fission and Fusion Developments and Prospects*, remarks made at the Council for the Advancement of Science Writing, Berkeley, 20 November 1969

Lyman Spitzer Jr., *The Stellerator*, Scientific American, Vol. 199 No. 4, October 1958 (page 28)

Index